The Eco-Management and Audit Scheme

A Practical Guide

Ruth Hillary

Imperial College of Science, Technology and Medicine

STANLEY THORNES

First published by Technical Communications (Publishing) Ltd

Reprinted in 1994 by:
Stanley Thornes (Publishers) Ltd
Ellenborough House
Wellington Street
CHELTENHAM
Glos. GL50 1YD
United Kingdom

Reprinted 1995

A catalogue record for this book is available from The British Library.

ISBN 0 7487 1900 8

Printed and bound in Great Britain by CIP, Basildon, Essex

CONTENTS

ACKNOWLEDGEMENTS   iii

FOREWORD   iv

EXECUTIVE SUMMARY   v

OVERVIEW OF THE ECO-MANAGEMENT AND AUDIT SCHEME   vi

ABOUT THE AUTHOR   vii

1   INTRODUCTION   1
     1.1   Increase in environmental pressures   1
     1.2   The EC's new approach to environmental policy   3
     1.3   Market-based tools   5
     1.4   Regulation – what is the significance?   6
     1.5   Legal basis for the Regulation   7
     1.6   Relationship with existing legislation   8
     1.7   Title and description of the Regulation's contents 8
     1.8   Terminology   10

2   THE ECO-MANAGEMENT AND AUDIT SCHEME EXPLAINED   11
     2.1   Origins and political progress   11
     2.2   Implementation timetable   13
     2.3   Objectives of the Eco-management and audit scheme   14
     2.4   Countries covered by the scheme   14
     2.5   Which companies can register?   15
     2.6   Should my company/site apply?   15

3   PUTTING IN PLACE THE ECO-MANAGEMENT AND
     AUDIT SCHEME   16
     3.1   Preparation for participation   16
     3.2   Site selection   17
     3.3   Writing a company environmental policy   18
     3.4   Undertaking the initial environmental review   22
     3.5   Defining a site's environmental programme   24
     3.6   Implementing an environmental management system   27
     3.7   Establishing an environmental audit programme   35
     3.8   Preparing an environmental statement   43

4   VALIDATION AND THE ACCREDITED ENVIRONMENTAL VERIFIERS   47
     4.1   Who are accredited environmental verifiers?   47
     4.2   Who accredits and supervises environmental verifiers? 49
     4.3   Applying to become an accredited environmental verifier 50
     4.4   Accreditation process   50
     4.5   Role of the accredited environmental verifier   52
     4.6   Accredited environmental verifier's relationship
           with the company   54
     4.7   Test cases   55

5	ORGANIZATIONS AND REGISTRATION	56
	5.1 Member State's functions and fees	56
	5.2 Dealings with the competent body – what is it and what does it do?	57
	5.3 Registration and de-registration procedures for companies	58
	5.4 Registration number and list of sites	60
	5.5 Cost of registration	60
	5.6 Relationship with enforcement authorities	60
	5.7 Role of the European Commission	61
6	LINKS WITH NATIONAL, EUROPEAN AND INTERNATIONAL STANDARDS	62
	6.1 Using standards	62
	6.2 Benefits of using BS 7750	62
	6.3 Links with BS 7750	63
	6.4 BS 7750: the new version	66
	6.5 Mandate for a European environmental management systems standard	66
7	BENEFITS AND PITFALLS OF THE ECO-MANAGEMENT AND AUDIT SCHEME	68
	7.1 Overview of the benefits and pitfalls	68
	7.2 Statement of participation	69
	7.3 Improving environmental performance	71
	7.4 Assurances for senior management	71
	7.5 Market-place benefits	72
	7.6 Special provision for small and medium-sized enterprises	72
	7.7 Exposing environmental liability	73
	7.8 Controlling environmental information	73
8	CASE STUDIES	74
	8.1 Eco-management and audit scheme applied to local authorities	74
	8.2 Lessons from the Eco-management and audit scheme pilot study	82
9	THE FUTURE	96
	9.1 Review of the Eco-management and audit scheme	96
	9.2 Could a voluntary scheme mutate into a mandatory one?	96
	9.3 Emerging business issues	97
APPENDIX 1	QUESTIONS AND ANSWERS	98
APPENDIX 2	SOURCES OF INFORMATION	103
	A2.1 Further reading	103
	A2.2 Useful contacts	104
APPENDIX 3	INDUSTRIAL ACTIVITIES COVERED	106
	A3.1 Other industrial activities	106
	A3.2 Statistical classification of economic activities (NACE) codes	106
APPENDIX 4	LIST OF ABBREVIATIONS	113

ACKNOWLEDGEMENTS

The author wishes to express her appreciation to Professor Janice Morphet of Woking Borough Council, Charles Duff of Norsk Hydro (UK) Ltd., Dr. Suzanne Geraty of Yamanouchi Ireland Co. Ltd., Leif Nørgaard and Lasse Simonsen of Novotex, Trish Marks of Birmingham City Council and Mike Lawford of Coats Viyella for their participation in the preparation of case study material for her report.

The author also extends her thanks to Dr. Paul Pritchard of Brown & Root Environmental for his useful comments on her report.

Special thanks to Dr. B. Delogu for his guidance on the Eco-management and audit scheme's purpose and contents during the author's time at the European Commission.

FOREWORD

by
Dr. B. Delogu
Directorate General XI
Environment, Nuclear Safety and Civil Protection
Commission of the European Communities

The occurrence of major environmental problems is due, in particular, to the failure of market mechanisms in this area: without the intervention of public powers the cost of pollution is seldom borne by polluters. This has necessitated massive recourse to regulations and standards, controls and inspections: the well known 'command and control' approach.

Complementary routes are now being explored, aimed at restoring as far as possible the market signals in the environmental field, and include the use of fiscal instruments, civil liability and promoting competition on the grounds of the environment. The Eco-management and audit scheme is an important Community initiative in the latter approach mentioned.

The fundamental objective of the scheme is to stimulate commitment by companies to continuous improvement of environmental performance of industrial activities and to promote the use by companies of best available environmental management tools, including environmental auditing.

The explanation of the scheme and its objectives to all potential participants, in particular small and medium-sized enterprises, is to be encouraged and welcomed. This report is a clear explanation of the Eco-management and audit scheme from a knowledgeable author and assists in the efforts needed to promulgate the details, aims and objectives of the scheme.

EXECUTIVE SUMMARY

A few proactive companies are already making the commitment to improve environmental performance and satisfy the public desire for more environmental information. The vast majority of enterprises, however, still struggle to effectively manage their environmental performance. The Eco-management and audit scheme aims to facilitate the implementation by companies of a structured, flexible and recognised approach to the management and improvement of their environmental performance.

This report sets out the Eco-management and audit scheme. It places it in the context of the EC's new approach to the environment outlined in the EC's 5th Action Program: *Towards Sustainability*. As a market-based tool, the scheme has the double benefits for businesses of being both voluntary, and embodying the spirit of self-regulation. Rewards are expected to come from the market.

The overall objective of the Regulation is to promote the continuous improvement of environmental performance by industry. It does this by committing a company to adopt environmental policies and sites to evaluate their environmental performance and provide relevant environmental information to the general public. This report clearly explains the details of the scheme, drawing on the practical experience gained during the scheme's pilot project.

Participation in the scheme is site-based and open to companies operating industrial activities. The report shows how, through pilot experience in the UK, the scheme's provisions have been extended to local government. Registration and de-registration procedures are outlined in the report.

Initial environmental reviews, environmental programmes, environmental management systems, environmental audits or audit cycles and environmental objectives are all detailed. Links with the British environmental management systems standard BS 7750 are also shown.

Accredited environmental verifiers, the new profession established by the scheme, are explained. Who they are, what they do and who supervises them are discussed in this report. Government responsibilities under the scheme and how they effect company participation are detailed. Relationships with HMIP and NRA and the roles of the European Commission and the new Regulatory Committee are also discussed.

Probably the most contentious aspect of the scheme, the public environmental statement, is outlined. The report illustrates how it could be an effective instrument for building both public and regulator trust in industry.

OVERVIEW OF THE
ECO-MANAGEMENT AND AUDIT SCHEME

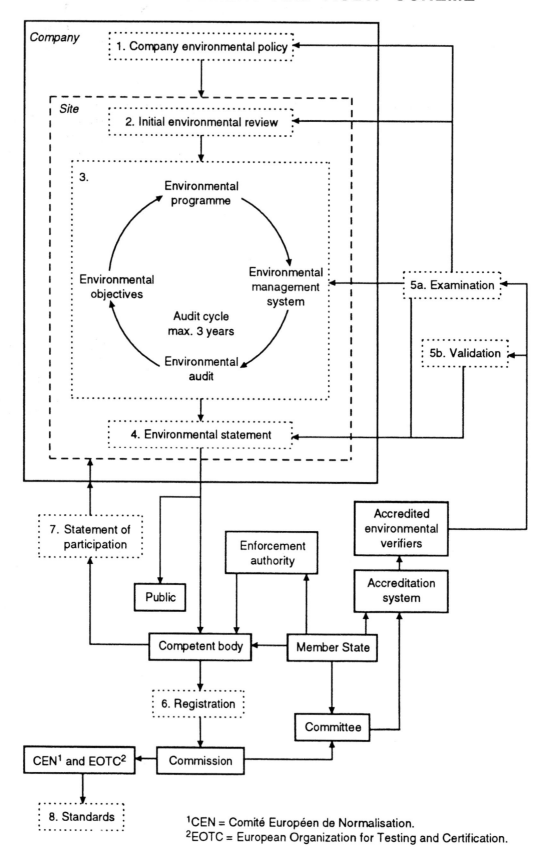

¹CEN = Comité Européen de Normalisation.
²EOTC = European Organization for Testing and Certification.

ABOUT THE AUTHOR

Ruth Hillary is a leading researcher of business environmental issues. She is based at the Centre for Environmental Technology, Imperial College, UK. In 1991 she undertook one of the first surveys of UK firms in the country: *Corporate Environmental Management Attitudes.*

Placed with the European Commission's Industry and Environment Division of DG XI (Environment), Ruth Hillary worked on the Eco-management and audit Regulation during its progress towards adoption and application. A considerable amount of her time was spent monitoring the company pilot project of the scheme.

Ruth Hillary has been actively involved in the pilot project of BS 7750, the environmental management systems standard, working closely with the Textiles and Textile Products Working Group. She has practical experience in undertaking both environmental reviews and environmental audits within industry.

Believing that many organizations were reinventing the wheel in the fields of environmental management and auditing, Ruth Hillary established the Environmental Management and Environmental Auditing Research Network (EM&EARN) as a forum to facilitate the exchange of ideas and practical experience between industry, policy makers and researchers. Since EM&EARN's establishment it has attracted support from the UK's ESRC (Economic and Social Research Council) Global Environmental Change Programme and held a number of very successful seminars on the Eco-management and audit scheme and BS 7750.

Ruth Hillary has published many articles on environmental management and the Eco-management and audit scheme. As the series editor for *The Business and the Environment Practitioner Series* she selects the current and emerging environmental topics and issues of importance to companies and presents them in a range of practical and readable reports.

CHAPTER 1

INTRODUCTION

1.1 Increase in environmental pressures

Increased legislative pressure, tougher regulatory bodies, diminishing insurance cover, greater public awareness and major environmental disasters have all conspired to propel environmental issues onto the business agenda (Figure 1.1). Government ministers expound to industry the virtues of business going green:

'Let me make no bones about it, one of the roots of my concerns for higher environmental standards, what ever their origin, is the future profitability and competitiveness of British business.' (Michael Heseltine, 1991)

and more recently:

'...those firms that recognise these realities and respond to them will survive and prosper in the cleaner and greener markets of the future. That is why I attach such importance to measures such as the proposed EC Eco-audit Regulation. (Michael Howard, 1993)

But generally, the integration of environmental issues into companies' general business framework has been slow and uneven, prompted more by the regulatory 'stick' than the profit 'carrot'.

Some businesses have responded to the burgeoning environmental challenge by developing environmental management systems. Many use codes of practices developed by industrial organizations such as the Confederation of British Industry (CBI) or the International Chamber of Commerce (ICC) to promote environmental commitments. The vast majority of enterprises, however, still lack the means to manage their environmental performance effectively.

This fact was reinforced by the author's recent survey of British businesses which sought to identify corporate environmental management attitudes. Over 1,420 managing directors of major companies in the UK were contacted with the aim of determining:

- the level of commitment to environmental strategy

- the degree of implementation of environmental management systems which make up the Eco-management and audit scheme

- the pressures driving businesses to undertake environmental audits.

1

Figure 1.1 – Pressures for company action on the environment

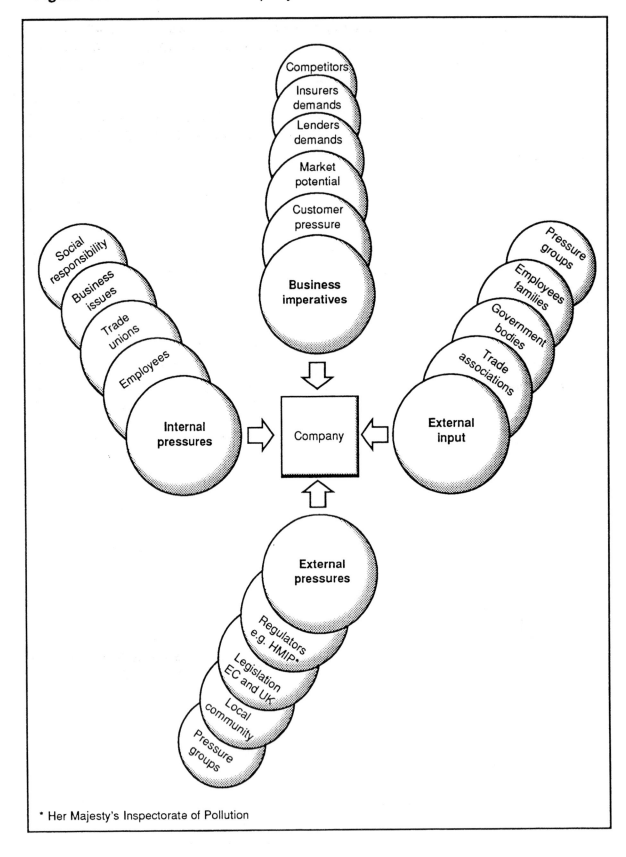

* Her Majesty's Inspectorate of Pollution

2

The key findings of the survey were:

- Businesses are increasingly aware of the need to outline broad environmental objectives in a company environmental policy but the minority of companies communicated this commitment to the public.

- Although the majority of companies assigned a person to oversee company environmental issues, reporting directly to the board or board member, few received backup training or additional resources to do the job.

- Few companies implemented environmental management systems or undertook environmental audits and consequently did not have many elements of the Eco-management and audit scheme in place.

- Most management actions on the environment were *ad hoc* and driven by environmental legislation and regulators such as Her Majesty's Inspectorate of Pollution (HMIP) and the National Rivers Authority (NRA).

Like any other aspect of a business, the environmental impacts of companies need to be effectively managed and controlled. Although most business managers may recognize the need to safeguard the environment in the abstract, few establish procedures or adopt strategies to translate the abstract into reality. In fact, in a recent survey of its members, the Institute of Directors found that most directors continue to view environmental issues as a threat rather than an opportunity.

The European Community's (EC) Eco-management and audit scheme was developed to facilitate management actions on the environment. It does this by providing companies with a structured and recognized approach to improve their environmental performance and satisfy the public need for more environmental information.

1.2 The EC's new approach to environmental policy

The Eco-management and audit scheme is set within the context of the EC's 5th Action Programme on the environment, *Towards Sustainability*.

Over the past two decades, the previous four EC action programmes on the environment have given rise to over 200 pieces of environmental legislation, covering such topics as water, air and soil pollution, nature protection and environmental impact assessments. The four programmes have achieved much, but still there is a slow and relentless deterioration of the general state of the environment. Consequently, it has become evident that to address environmental issues in Europe, EC environmental policy needs to be more far-reaching and effective. *Towards Sustainability* outlines the EC's new approach to the environment.

Central to the EC's 5th Action Programme are the basic principles of sustainable development: preventive and precautionary action and shared responsibility. The strategy to achieve the Programme's principles relies on the integration of the environment into other policies and depends on the ability to adopt progressive environmental measures. Within this framework the Programme endorses the strategy of tackling five key sectors in a co-ordinated and comprehensive way.

The priority sectors are:

• Industry • Energy • Transport • Tourism • Agriculture

The Programme, which runs from the beginning of 1993 to the year 2000, also proposes broadening the range of instruments to complement existing normative or 'command and control' legislation which is typified by controls of discharges to atmosphere, water or land and environmental quality standards.

'Command and control' succinctly describes the operation of such environmental legislation because while the legislation sets the environmental standards for a certain process or operation (the 'command' part), inspection is necessary by enforcement authorities to ensure compliance to the standards, the 'control' part. 'Command and control' legislation has certain advantages and disadvantages.

Advantages of 'command and control' legislation include:

• guaranteed levels of protection across the EC

• harmonization in the level of protection throughout the EC.

Disadvantages of 'command and control' legislation include:

• often only minimum environmental standards can be set

• standards quickly become out-of-date

• not all environmental effects can be covered

• company creativity is not harnessed.

Considerable resources are required for the control part of 'command and control' legislation. Member States of the EC must invest both financial and human resources to monitor, inspect and sometimes punish those organizations subjected to traditional environmental legislation. Since resources are not infinite and the financial cake needs to be subdivided amongst many competing interests, controls cannot be comprehensive in any of the Member States, although some are more effective than others.

Similarly, Member States have different degrees of expertise and resources to implement EC environmental legislation, resulting in a varied record of implementation of the different environmental laws.

The new range of instruments outlined in the EC's 5th Action Programme include:

- horizontal supporting instruments

- financial support mechanisms

- market-based instruments.

Horizontal supporting instruments focus on improving planning, increasing information to both the public and the consumer and increasing training and education. Base line and statistical data are to be improved and scientific research and technological development strengthened, particularly in the areas of less polluting technologies and technologies and techniques that solve current environmental problems.

Financial support mechanisms centre on direct EC budgetary actions which have environmental objectives such as LIFE (Community Financial Instrument for the Environment). All other budgetary plans, especially structural funds directed at regional development and known for their dubious environmental record, will be encouraged to incorporate environmental considerations and environmental legislation.

1.3   Market-based tools

Market-based instruments offer probably the most innovative development in the EC's 5th Action Programme on the environment. Designed to internalize external environmental costs, market-based tools alert both producers and consumers to the need to use natural resources responsibly and minimize or avoid pollution and waste.

Essentially, market-based tools are about 'getting the prices right' so that environmentally friendlier products and processes are rewarded in the market place. Market-based tools are expected to harness the creative energies of companies and direct them towards improving the environmental performance of products and processes in a way which has remained untapped by the traditional 'command and control' style of environmental legislation.

The Eco-management and audit scheme is a market-based tool developed to introduce market forces in the environmental field by promoting competition between industrial activities on environmental grounds. Eco-labelling for products is another example of a market-based Regulation.

As an essentially untested method of achieving environmental improvements, the scheme is an innovative piece of EC legislation. The implicit assumption is that the market will reward companies for participating in the scheme and as a result, market pressure will encourage an increasing number of firms to join. Thus, company energies will be tapped and environmental performance improved.

1.4 Regulation – what is the significance?

A number of legal instruments are used by the Commission when drafting legislation. These include, for example, a Resolution, a Decision, a Directive and a Regulation. Most EC environmental legislation appears as Directives which require national legislation to be passed to implement their provisions and make them effective.

The Eco-management and audit scheme is a Regulation. Regulations, unlike Directives, become directly applicable in national law as soon as they are adopted by the Council of Ministers (see Figure 1.2). There is no need for Member State governments to enact national legislation. The Regulation's text, published in the *Official Journal* of the EC, is the text that will be used throughout the 12 Member States.

Figure 1.2 – *EC Institutions and procedures*

Commission of the European Communities, normally referred to simply as the Commission, is the civil service of the EC and is responsible for proposing legislation.

Council of Ministers, normally referred to as the Council, is the political arm of the EC, made up of ministers from the 12 Member States and is responsible for adopting legislation. Depending on what topics are being discussed in the Council of Ministers, different national ministers will attend. The Eco-management and audit scheme was discussed by environment ministers and therefore the Council of Minister shorthand in this case is the Environment Council.

European Parliament, made up of elected members (MEPs) from the 12 countries, is assisted by parliamentary committees of MEPs which undertake initial discussions of Commission proposals. The Eco-management and audit scheme was discussed in the Committee on the Environment, Public Health and Consumer Protection.

Some Regulations have a delay or implementation time period written into their text which means that after their adoption they effectively apply at a later date in the 12 Member States. The Eco-management and audit Regulation has an implementation period of 21 months.

Positive and significant benefits exist for companies because the scheme is a Regulation.

Two benefits are:

1.   The text of the Regulation applies across the 12 Member States of the EC which means that a company applying the scheme in the UK will work to the same text as a company applying the scheme in, say, Italy or Germany. Regulation status has thus created 'a level playing field'. No distortion or unfair competitive advantage can be achieved by companies working to different versions of the scheme, which could have been the case if the scheme had been a Directive and each Member State had interpreted it into national law in a different way.

2.   The scheme is open to company participation at exactly the same time across the EC, preventing competitive disadvantage for companies situated in Member States which are slow at implementing EC legislation.

Concern has been expressed in some business quarters that using a Regulation for a voluntary scheme is a contradiction. This is not the case.

As a Regulation, Member States must have the scheme in place for voluntary company participation but once companies join they must follow all the Regulation's requirements. The purpose of using a Regulation for the scheme was to achieve the two benefits noted above and was directed at controlling Member States.

1.5   Legal basis for the Regulation

Article 130s of the Treaty of Rome, as modified by the Single European Act in 1987, is the legal basis for the Eco-management and audit Regulation.   Two important conditions are set by the scheme's legal basis:

1.   The opinions of the European Parliament and the Economic and Social Committee are required before the Council of Ministers can adopt the Regulation.

2.   Unanimity is required for the scheme's adoption by Council, i.e., all 12 Member States must agree to the Regulation.

The scheme's legal basis meant that delays entered its adoption. When the Maastricht treaty is finally ratified by all 12 Member States, legislation framed under Article 130s will not require unanimity. Consequently, the Eco-management and audit scheme's review by Council will be by qualified majority voting, and as a result, one country will not have the power to block its progress.

1.6 Relationship with existing legislation

The Eco-management and audit scheme does not replace existing Community or national environmental legislation or technical standards and does in no way remove a company's responsibility to fulfil all its legal obligations under such legislation or standards.

1.7 Title and description of the Regulation's contents

The Regulation's full title is:

Council Regulation (EEC) No 1836/93 of 29 June 1993 allowing voluntary participation by companies in the industrial sector in a Community eco-management and audit scheme.

The Regulation appeared in the *Official Journal* of the EC on 10th July 1993 (Ref. *OJ* L168 Vol. 36) and consisted of 21 Articles and five Annexes. The following, Tables 1.1 and 1.2, detail these and briefly describe their content.

Table 1.1 – Eco-management and audit Regulation's articles

Article number	Title and description of article
Article 1	*The Eco-management and audit scheme and its objectives* Defines the scheme's aims and relationship with existing environmental laws.
Article 2	*Definitions* Defines the 15 terms used in the Regulation, e.g. site, environmental audit, industrial activity and accredited environmental verifier.
Article 3	*Participation in the scheme* Explains the elements a site must undertake to become registered on the scheme.
Article 4	*Auditing and validation* Outlines who may conduct a site's internal environmental audit, how and at what frequency, and details accredited environmental verifiers' activities.
Article 5	*Environmental statement* Lists the information required in a statement and explains simplified annual statements.
Article 6	*Accreditation and supervision of environmental verifiers* Defines accreditation systems for environmental verifiers which Member States are required to establish.
Article 7	*List of accredited environmental verifiers* Define frequency of lists and where they should be published.
Article 8	*Registration of sites* Explains site registration and de-registration by the competent body.
Article 9	*Publication of the list of registered sites* Defines how lists of registered sites should be published in the EC's *Official Journal.*

Table 1.1 – continued

Article number	Title and description of article
Article 10	*Statement of participation* Defines where sites may use the statement.
Article 11	*Costs and fees* Allows Member States to set up charges.
Article 12	*Relationship with national, European and international standards* Explains under what conditions standards may be used in conjunction with the scheme.
Article 13	*Promotion of companies' participation, in particular of small and medium-sized enterprises* States how Member States may promote company involvement in the scheme.
Article 14	*Inclusion of other sectors* Defines under what conditions other sectors may be included.
Article 15	*Information* Defines how Member States may promote and publicize the scheme.
Article 16	*Infringements* Gives Member States powers to act in cases of non-compliance with the Regulation.
Article 17	*Annexes* States that the Annexes may be adapted before the Regulation's review date.
Article 18	*Competent bodies* Defines and ensures the neutrality of the competent body.
Article 19	*Committee* Sets up the structure and voting procedure for the Committee.
Article 20	*Revision* Sets the time limit for the Commission review of the entire Regulation.
Article 21	*Entry into force* Gives the dates when the Regulation enters into force and when it will apply in the Member States.

Table 1.2 – Eco-management and audit Regulation's annexes

Annex number	Description of annex
Annex I	Details the requirements for a company's environmental policy and a site's environmental objectives and programmes, environmental management systems similar to BS 7750 and good management practices.
Annex II	Details the requirements concerning site environmental auditing, its methodology, coverage and frequency.
Annex III	Details the accreditation criteria for environmental verifiers and their functions and actions during verification.
Annex IV	Shows four examples of the statement of participation with its graphic symbol which may be used to advertise participation in the scheme.
Annex V	Lists the information that needs to be supplied to the competent body in an application for registration on the scheme.

1.8   Terminology

Throughout this report the Regulation, i.e., the complete law with its preamble, articles and annexes, published in the European Commission's *Official Journal* is referred to as the Eco-management and audit Regulation whereas the Eco-management and audit scheme is used when discussing the elements and workings of the Regulation.

Confusion will no doubt develop as a variety of acronyms appear. Some that are already in circulation (and their origins) are listed as follows:

- CEMAS   Community Eco-management and audit scheme

- EMAR   Eco-management and audit Regulation

- EMAS   Eco-management and audit scheme (used by BSI)

- EMA   Community Eco-management and audit scheme (used by the UK Department of Trade and Industry and the Department of the Environment).

The scheme's original name, Eco-audit scheme, is often still used – especially in EC countries other than the UK.

CHAPTER 2

THE ECO-MANAGEMENT AND AUDIT SCHEME EXPLAINED

2.1 Origins and political progress

Set within the framework of the EC's 5th Action Programme on the environment, the Eco-management and audit scheme was first released by the Commission as a consultation document in December 1990, at which time it was referred to as the Eco-audit scheme. The scheme was unique in Europe and possibly the world as being the first piece of environmental legislation to define a system which included both environmental auditing and public reporting of environmental information.

Subsequent discussions on the consultation document between the 12 Member States produced eight different drafts of the scheme and introduced a number of modifications before it was finally published as a Commission proposal in the EC's *Official Journal* on March 27, 1992. The type of changes introduced to the Commission's original consultation document included:

- a change in legal instrument from Directive to Regulation

- a change from mandatory company participation to voluntary participation

- the removal of Member States' power to compel certain industries to use the scheme

- the alteration in the frequency of environmental auditing.

After publication as a Commission proposal, the scheme entered the arena of political negotiations between the 12 Member States in preparation for agreement and adoption by the Council of Ministers. Figure 2.1 summarizes the legislative process. Many technical working group meetings were convened, consisting of representatives from each Member State and the Commission and chaired by the country which held the current Presidency of the EC.

In parallel with Council negotiations, opinions of both the European Parliament and the Economic and Social Committee (EcoSoc) were being formed. Both were required before adoption was possible by Council. The Economic and Social Committee gave its positive opinion on the scheme on the 20th October 1992. The European Parliament discussed the scheme in Committee in late 1992, finally voting at the European Parliamentary plenary session in Strasbourg on January 19, 1993. It supported the Commission's proposal with 75 of its own amendments to the text.

Figure 2.1 – *EC legislative process for the Eco-management and audit scheme*

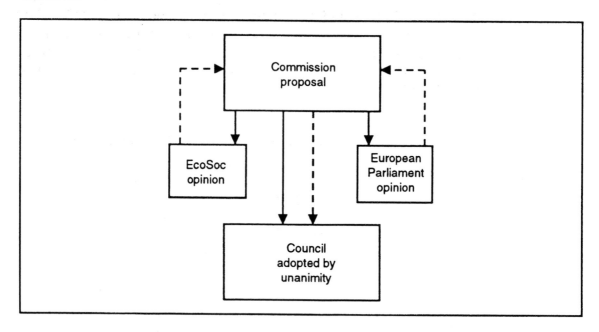

The Commission accepted 51 of the parliamentary amendments and rewrote its own proposal of 27th March 1992. The modified Commission proposal was published on 16th March 1993 (Reference COM(93) 97 final) and submitted to Council for consideration. They chose to ignore it. The modified proposal is *not* the adopted Regulation; do not use it.

The UK government had afforded the scheme considerable support since it was first released as a consultation paper; consequently, under its Presidency, from July to December 1992, the government listed it as one of its presidential priorities and made strenuous efforts to achieve its adoption.

Adoption was not achieved during the UK presidency but was blocked for two reasons:

1.   The Regulation's adoption required unanimity, i.e., all 12 Member States must agree to it because its legal basis is Article 130s (see Section 1.5). At the UK's last Environment Council meeting only 11 countries reached agreement on the scheme. Germany held a general reservation on the proposal and therefore blocked agreement.

2.   The opinion of the European Parliament had not yet been given.

Adoption of the Eco-management and audit Regulation eluded the British presidency but the Danish, who held the subsequent presidency (January to June 1993), maintained the momentum behind the scheme. The proposal was at the top of their agenda for their first Environment Council meeting on March 22 and 23, 1993. All technical hitches had been removed. The only barrier to agreement was Germany's general reservation on the scheme.

Tough negotiations and pressure from the other 11 countries during the Council meeting finally led to Germany lifting its general reservation with only three modifications. The tabled text was accepted on March 23. The Regulation was tabled for formal adoption at the June 28/29, 1993 Environment Council meeting, the second and last under the Danish presidency. Adoption at this meeting was a mere formality and was achieved on June 29, 1993 (see Table 2.1).

Table 2.1 – *Political progress of the Eco-management and audit scheme*

Political Progress	Date
Released as a consultation document	December 1990
Published as a Commission proposal in the *Official Journal* (Ref. C76 Vol. 35)	27 March 1992
Economic and Social Committee opinion given	20 October 1992
European Parliament opinion given	19 January 1993
Modified Commission proposal published (ignore) (Ref. COM(93) 97 final)	16 March 1993
Environment Council unanimous political agreement	23 March 1993
Adoption of the Regulation	29 June 1993
Publication of Regulation in EC's *Official Journal* (Ref. L168 Vol. 36)	10th July 1993

2.2   Implementation timetable

The Regulation entered into force in all 12 Member States on the 13th July, 1993, three days after its publication in the EC's *Official Journal*. There is a 21 month implementation period before the Regulation becomes effective and open to company participation. This 21 month period is to allow each Member State to prepare the administration necessary for the scheme's operation, such as setting up a competent body. This means that the first companies registering on the scheme will not appear until April 1995 (see Table 2.2); however, companies may now start putting in place the provisions of the scheme in preparation for registration.

Table 2.2 – *Regulation's timetable*

Action on Regulation	Date
Adoption date by Environmental Council	29 June 1993
Entry into force in 12 Member States	13 July 1993
Applies and open to company participation	10 April 1995
Final review date for regulation by council	13 July 1998

2.3 Objectives of the Eco-management and audit scheme

The Eco-management and audit scheme was established for the evaluation and improvement of industrial activities' environmental performance and the provision of environmental information to the public. Its overall objective is to promote *continuous environmental performance improvements* within industry by committing sites to:

- establish and implement environmental policies, programmes and management systems

- periodically evaluate in a systematic and objective way the performance of the site elements

- provide environmental performance information to the public.

2.4 Countries covered by the scheme

As a piece of EC legislation, the Eco-management and audit Regulation applies to all 12 Member States. Any company operating an industrial site within the EC can apply to the scheme.

The EC Member States are:

Belgium	Greece	Portugal
Denmark	Ireland	Spain
France	Italy	The Netherlands
Germany	Luxembourg	UK

Although the Regulation's jurisdiction is limited to the 12 Member States, there is nothing to stop companies in other countries using the scheme's elements as a way of managing and improving their environmental performance. Such companies could *not* register a non-EC located site on the scheme but they could acknowledge their adherence to it in the statement of participation (see Section 7.2).

A number of governments and companies located outside the EC have expressed interest in the Eco-management and audit scheme and it is likely that multinational companies registering EC-based sites will extend the scheme's elements to non-EC sites. EFTA (European Free Trade Association) countries have an agreement with the EC on the transferability of EC environmental legislation into their national legislation. Some EFTA countries, for example Norway, may adopt the scheme directly into their own national legislation.

2.5 Which companies can register?

Broadly speaking, the industrial base of the EC is covered by the Eco-management and audit scheme. Company participation in the Regulation is voluntary and restricted to companies performing industrial activities.

> **Industrial activity definition**
>
> Any activity listed under sections C and D of the EC classification of economic activities in the EC (NACE rev. 1); with the addition of electricity, gas, steam and hot water production and the recycling, treatment, destruction or disposal of solid or liquid waste.

Section C of the NACE codes covers mining and quarrying and section D covers manufacturing. Appendix 3 of this report provides the detailed groups of industrial activities listed under the NACE codes.

Inclusion of non-industrial sectors

A late introduction into the scheme was the inclusion of other non-industrial sectors. Certain Member States, in particular the UK, were keen to see the extension of the Eco-management and audit scheme to non-industrial sectors and has undertaken a pilot study to investigate how it applies to local authorities (see Section 8.1).

As a compromise, Member States are allowed to apply the elements of the Eco-management and audit scheme to other sectors as long as it is on an experimental basis only. The non-industrial sectors specifically mentioned as examples are the distributive trades and public services.

2.6 Should my company/site apply?

Before senior management decides to register a site on the scheme, certain issues need to be considered. Management should be able to answer yes to the following questions:

- Is the selected site maintaining full compliance with EC and national environmental legislative requirements?

- Is the company willing to devote, and continue to devote, the necessary human and financial resources to the scheme?

- Is top company management committed to applying the scheme?

- Is the site ready to disclose environmental performance information to the public?

CHAPTER 3

PUTTING IN PLACE THE ECO-MANAGEMENT AND AUDIT SCHEME

Implementation of the Eco-management and audit scheme occurs at two levels: the company and the site. Figure 3.1 outlines the various stages of the scheme, while the text explains the details. In this report, definitions from the Regulation are shown in grey shading.

Figure 3.1 – *Implementation stages of the Eco-management and audit scheme*

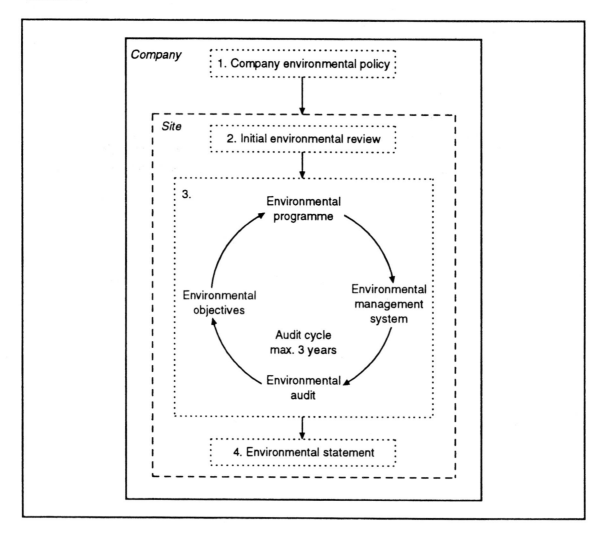

3.1   Preparation for participation

Before taking steps to apply the Eco-management and audit scheme, a company needs to ensure it has the necessary building blocks in place for the process to be successful. These include:

- Top level management commitment and board support clearly communicated throughout the company.

- Sufficient human and financial resources allocated to implementing and maintaining the scheme (easily underestimated).

- The understanding and support of all employees regarding the scheme's aims.

- The requirement that the scheme fits with existing management systems and is not viewed as burdensome.

- The willingness of management to disclose, to the public, environmental performance information.

3.2 Site selection

Unless a multisite company is going to register all its sites at once on the Eco-management and audit scheme, site selection is necessary. Company management will need to determine which site or sites are initially most suitable for registration on the scheme. Management will need to consider a range of criteria.

Range of site selection criteria

- compliance record of the site with environmental legislation and standards

- existing environmental performance at the site

- commitment of local site management to participation

- motivation of staff at the site

- available human and financial resources for participation

- industrial activities at the site

- size of the site

- location of the site

- existing environmental procedures which could assist the site, such as applications for authorization for prescribed processes to HMIP or local authorities.

Company management needs to select a site which they feel can successfully implement the provisions of the scheme and act as a flag ship for other company sites. Test run the implementation of the scheme and build site management confidence before going public.

> **Site definition**
>
> All land on which the industrial activities under the control of a company at a given location are carried out, including any connected or associated storage or raw materials, by-products, intermediate products, end products and waste material, and any equipment and infrastructure involved in the activities, whether or not fixed.

Concern has been expressed about the Regulation's definition of a site. In particular, companies involved in the pilot programme have questioned the validity of the site definition where several autonomous subsidiary companies shared the same location or the same facility such as a waste treatment plant. Relationships where a company leases part of a site or a building on a site and ownership of the site all raise issues for management wanting to register a site on the scheme.

The key element in the site definition which controls the extent of a site is management's control over the operations, i.e., if management has direct responsibility for activities then those activities delimit the site. It does not matter if the site is owned or rented by the company or whether other firms lease its buildings or land. Site land is drawn by management control, not by the perimeter fence.

3.3 Writing a company environmental policy

Once a company has taken the decision to prepare one or more of its sites for registration on the Eco-management and audit scheme, its first action (Box 1 in Figure 3.1, is to write and adopt a company environmental policy. Single site companies will also need a company environmental policy.

> **Company definition**
>
> The organization which has overall management control over activities at a given site

> **Environmental policy definition**
>
> The company's overall aims and principles of action with respect to the environment including compliance with all relevant regulatory requirements regarding the environment.

The environmental policy must fulfil two requirements:

1.   Provide for compliance with all relevant environmental regulatory requirements.

2.   Have clear commitments aimed at the continuous improvement of environmental performance.

Limits are set on how far a company has to go to reduce its environmental impacts. Reductions do not have to exceed levels which can be achieved by the economically viable application of best available technologies. An EC version of the UK's Best Available Techniques Not Entailing Excessive Cost (BATNEEC).

Considerable discussion has centred on the meanings and differences between 'continuous' and 'continual' improvement of environmental performance. Dictionary definitions state that 'continuous' means uninterrupted and 'continual' means frequently reoccurring. In a perfect world, where environmental improvement is measured at all points throughout all time periods, the two words could be graphically represented, as shown in Table 3.1.

Table 3.1 *'Continuous' and 'Continual'*

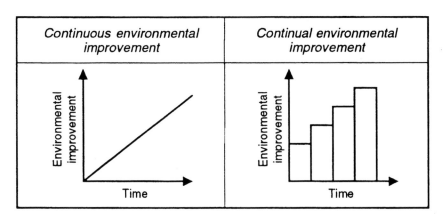

In practice, the distinction between the two types of improvement is immaterial as it is impossible to achieve a perfect improvement measuring regime. Consequently, only continual environmental performance improvements can be demonstrated. **The important issue for businesses is to show improvement, over time, of environmental performance.**

Requirements for the company environmental policy are detailed in Annex I of the Regulation. The company environmental policy should be:

•   written

•   adopted at the highest management level

- periodically reviewed and appropriately revised, especially in the light of environmental audit findings, at the highest management level

- publicly available.

A company's environmental policy must be based on eleven 'principles of action'. These are referred to as Good Management Practices outlined in Annex I.D. of the Regulation, and cover a wide range of topics such as employees, products, pollution, waste, environmental accidents, the public, contractors and customers. The company's activities should be regularly checked to establish that they are consistent with these principles and the objective of continuous environmental performance improvements.

Good management practices – basis for a policy

1. Foster a sense of responsibility for the environment at all employee levels.

2. Assess the environmental impact before all new activities, products and processes are undertaken.

3. Monitor and assess the impact of current activities on the local environment and examine any significant impacts on the general environment.

4. Undertake measures to prevent or eliminate pollution. Where this is not feasible, undertake measures, taking account of the possible clean technologies, to reduce pollution and waste to the minimum and conserve resources.

5. Take measures to prevent accidental emissions of materials or energy.

6. Establish monitoring procedures, including documented measurement and testing, to check compliance with the company environmental policy.

7. Establish and implement procedures and actions in the case of non-compliance with the company environmental policy.

8. Co-operate with the public authorities when establishing and updating contingency procedures for minimizing the impact of any accidental discharges to the environment that may occur.

9. Pursue an open dialogue with the public and provide the public with enough information to enable them to understand the environmental impact of the company's activities.

10. Provide customers with adequate advice about the environmental aspects of handling, using and disposing of the company's products.

11. The company must ensure that contractors, working at the site on their behalf, apply the same environmental standards as the company.

As well as the Good Management Practices, a company's environmental policy should address the environmental, production, publicity and staffing issues outlined in Annex I.C. of the Regulation and listed in Section 3.4.

Environmental policies should avoid bland 'motherhood' statements and waffle. A good example of a clear and direct policy signed and supported by the chief executive is Coats Viyella's Corporate Environmental Policy shown in Figure 3.2. Coats Viyella is a highly decentralized company with over 250 sites across Europe. Its environmental policy acts as an umbrella policy with each operating company being encouraged to develop their own policy adapted to country and activity-specific conditions, and supported by local management. Ownership of each policy is with the local workforce who can identify with its commitments.

Figure 3.2 – *An environmental policy for Coats Viyella*

Coats Viyella recognizes that environmental issues are of fundamental importance to a successful and responsible business strategy.
Therefore we are committed to minimizing the environmental impact of our operations wherever and whenever possible. In line with our commitment to the environment, Coats Viyella will:
1
Ensure that its operations comply with the existing legislation of the countries in which it operates.
2
Deal with all environmental issues either at, or as close to, their source as is practically possible.
3
Strive to design and develop products which have the minimum environmental impacts during their manufacture, use and subsequent disposal.
4
Minimize energy usage and waste wherever possible and practical.
5
Re-cycle materials wherever possible and practical.
6
Set environmental targets which it will strive to achieve. These targets will be integrated into the day to day running of all our businesses.
7
Train and educate its workforce in the relevant aspects of environmental best practices.
8
Communicate its environmental policy and practices at all levels and at all sites of the organization.
9
Review its environmental policy on a regular basis.

Figure 3.3 – *Coats Viyella's approach to the environment*

Coats Viyella firmly believes that good business practice and concern for the environment can and should go hand in hand. The key to tackling environmental issues successfully is pollution prevention at source by:-

A. CONSUMING LESS raw materials, in the production process, hence lowering costs and reducing emissions.

B. RE-FORMULATING to more environmentally friendly products and processes so as to avoid the need for expensive and complex 'end of pipe' treatments and 'clean up' processes.

N.C. BAIN

Chief Executive

WHO CARES WINS

MANAGING FOR A

BETTER ENVIRONMENT

3.4 Undertaking the initial environmental review

After a company has adopted an overall company policy and selected a site to implement the provisions of the Eco-management and audit scheme, the first action at the site is to undertake an initial environmental review (Box 2 in Figure 3.1).

> Environmental review definition
>
> An initial comprehensive analysis of the environmental issues, impact and performance related to activities at a site.

No review methodology is explained in the Regulation but the scope of issues to be covered by the environmental review are outlined in Annex I.C. (The environmental policy addresses the same issues.)

Issues to be addressed by the initial environmental review

1. Assessment, control and reduction of the impact of the activity concerned on the various sectors of the environment.

2. Energy management, saving and choice.

3. Raw materials management, saving, choice and transportation as well as water management and savings.

4. Waste avoidance, recycling, reuse, transportation and disposal.

5. Evaluation, control and reduction of noise within and outside the site.

6. Selection of new production processes and changes to production processes.

7. Product planning (design, packaging, transportation, use and disposal).

8. Environmental performance and practices of contractors, subcontractors and suppliers.

9. Prevention and limitation of environmental accidents.

10. Contingency procedures in cases of environmental accidents.

11. Staff information and training on environmental issues.

12. External information on environmental issues.

Many companies use a combination of interviews with site personnel, inspection of documents including site plans and maps and on-site observations to determine the base line data of an environmental review. Staff undertaking the review should be independent of the site to ensure objectivity; however, the review should not be portrayed as a policing exercise but should encourage staff participation.

Often companies refer to their initial environmental review as an environmental audit and in fact the methodologies used are very similar. But in a review, the receiver collects baseline data and therefore has to decide how far to go with data collection. Basic areas for investigation are provided in the previous list; however, an effective review does not just focus on the present site situation. Additional areas that would be useful to address include:

•   Site history to identify a possible legacy of environmental problems, especially contamination of land.

•   Environmental setting, particularly to identify land use and drinking water sources, residents' locations and local facilities such as schools and sensitive natural habitats such as national parks.

Questionnaires can be constructed in a variety of ways but basically they are developed to aid the accurate collection of information and to ease compilation and analysis of information. The following two tables, Table 3.2 and Table 3.3, show excerpts of the different approaches companies take to gathering review information.

To assist the data collection process inventories may be developed for emissions, liquid effluent, waste and storage of chemicals. Table 3.4 illustrates the type of inventory headings used to collect information in a tabular form.

Table 3.2 – *Summarized list of issues and questions*

Basic area	Information gathered from the review
Environmental policy	Is the policy up-to-date? Is the policy appropriate to the business and does it cover all the relevant environmental issues? Has the policy been distributed internally and how widely? Is the policy available to the public? Action: obtain a copy of the policy.
Management	Has a person been designated to be responsible for environmental issues? Is that person clear of his/her responsibilities? Are the site's environmental issues a regular agenda item at Board/Management meetings?
Legislation	Is the company aware of the environmental legislation and standards applying to its activities? Action: obtain a copy of the legislation register. Are there statutory limits for air emissions, effluent discharges, waste, noise? Have there been any cases of non-compliance with the set limits? What corrective action was taken? Was the regulatory body informed?
Emergency procedures	Is there a documented procedure for dealing with major environmental incidents? Where is it housed? Are employees aware of the procedures?

When undertaking the initial environmental review it is important that the review is comprehensive so that subsequent elements of the scheme are built on a strong foundation of accurate data and information.

3.5 Defining a site's environmental programme

In light of the results from the environmental review, site management is required to introduce a site-specific environmental programme (Box 3 of Figure 3.1). A hybrid, the environmental programme is aimed at delivering company environmental policy commitments towards continuous environmental performance improvements but tailored to site-specific circumstances.

A site's programme must address site-specific environmental issues, making sure all the issues in Annex I.C. of the Regulation are covered (listed in Section 3.4), and define objectives and actions to deliver greater environmental protection.

Table 3.3 – *Review questionnaire form*

Environmental topic:	Department:	Name of interviewee:		Date:

Questions	Answer	Yes	No	N/A
Who is responsible for waste management?				
Are staff aware of legislation covering waste e.g. Duty of care?				
What wastes are generated from this department? List				
Are there any hazardous wastes?				
Are any wastes recycled?				
What disposal routes are used for the waste? e.g. on-site, landfill, incineration				
Are waste records kept? View				
Have any breaches occurred of waste disposal permits?				
Were authorities informed?				
What corrective actions were taken?				
Are contractors used for waste disposal?				
Have site staff visited the contractor's disposal site?				
Where are waste consignment notes housed? View				

Table 3.4 – *Example inventories topic headings*

Air emission inventory topic headings						
Air emission source	Licensed	Monitored	Control device	Efficiency of device	Disposal of pollutant	Maintenance programme
Waste inventory topic headings						
Waste type	Source of waste	Volume	Control	Treatment	Transport	Disposal
Liquid effluent inventory topic headings						
Liquid discharge	Consent	Volume	Monitored	Treatment	Discharged to	Disposal route

Environmental programme definition

A description of the company's specific objectives and activities to ensure greater protection of the environment at a given site, including a description of the measures taken or envisaged to achieve such objectives and where appropriate the deadlines set for implementation of such measures.

A site's programme should outline in writing the following:

• objectives and activities to enhance environmental protection

• personnel responsible at each level and function of the company for the programme's objectives

• actions and the means to achieve the objectives and activities

• appropriate implementation deadlines.

Additional environmental programmes

While the site will normally have just one environmental programme, additional specific programmes will need to be established under the following conditions:

- new developments

- new or modified products

- new or modified services

- new or modified processes.

Each of the specific programmes will need to define the following elements:

- environmental objectives for the new or modified activity

- measures to achieve the objectives

- procedures for dealing with change as the new or modified project develops

- inbuilt corrective mechanisms which need to show how they will be activated and how their efficiency will be measured for the circumstances which arise.

3.6 Implementing an environmental management system

Site management must establish and implement, for all the activities at the site, an environmental management system.

Environmental management system definition

That part of the overall management system which includes the organizational structure, responsibilities, practices, procedures, processes and resources for determining and implementing the environmental policy.

Organizations already implementing BSI's environmental management systems standard (BS 7750) will be pleased to note that large parts of BS 7750 are specified in Annex I.B. of the Regulation (see Section 6.3).

The environmental management system must be designed, implemented and maintained to address the following requirements:

1. Environmental policy, objectives and programmes.

2. Organization and personnel

3. Environment effects.

4. Operational control.

5.   Environmental management documentation records.

6.   Environmental audits.

1. Environmental policy, objectives and programmes

Management, at the highest appropriate level, must establish and periodically review the environmental policy, objectives and programmes for a site. No guidelines are provided about what level of management is 'appropriate'. It would be sensible, however, for a company's environmental policy review to be overseen by the board or a board member since this, along with the site's programme, will be in the public domain.

2. Organisation and personnel

• Defined and documented key personnel whose work affects the environment.

• Appoint a management representative with responsibility for overseeing the implementation of the system.

• Ensure staff awareness of:

(i)   importance of compliance with the environmental policy and objective

(ii) potential environmental effects of their work and benefits from improved performance

(iii) roles and responsibilities for compliance with policy, objectives and system

(iv) possible consequences of ignoring operating procedures.

• Identify and provide appropriate training for staff whose work could significantly affect the environment.

The company is required to respond to enquiries from 'relevant interested parties', both employees and non-employees, on the company's environmental effects and management, and thus procedures are required to receive, respond to and document such enquiries. 'Relevant interested party' is not defined.

3. Environmental effects

Evaluation of environmental effects and their compilation into a register has already caused much discussion amongst organizations participating in the

BS 7750 pilot project. This is principally because there is no clear indication of what is a significant environmental effect or how far outside the site boundary the environment has to be considered. For example, do CO_2 emissions need to be considered at a global level to determine their significance?

Nevertheless, a register needs to be compiled of the environmental effects of the site's activities, taking into account a variety of operating conditions. Although the Regulation does not define 'environmental effect' the BS 7750 definition does provide some guidance. It is 'any direct or indirect impingement of the activities, products and services of the organisation upon the environment, whether adverse or beneficial'.

The environmental effects register must consider the following issues unless they are not appropriate to the site:

1.   Emissions to atmosphere, both controlled and uncontrolled.

2.   Discharges to water or sewers, both controlled and uncontrolled.

3.   All waste including hazardous waste.

4.   Land contamination.

5.   Natural resource use, including use of land, water, fuels and energy.

6.   Visual impact and discharge of thermal energy, noise, odour, dust and vibration.

7.   Effects on specific parts of the environment and ecosystem.

The register should also include the environmental effects under a variety of operating conditions:

1.   Normal operating conditions.

2.   Abnormal operating conditions.

3.   Accidents and potential emergency situations.

4.   Past, current and planned activities.

Companies tackling the issue of the environmental effects register during the BS 7750 pilot did not want a standard format for the register but did identify that more guidance was required to establish what were the significant effects for a sector. Implementing organizations were comfortable with the time period (past, present and future) of the register but used a variety of approaches to establish environmental effects and significance.

Common to all approaches was a list of environmental issues which were then weighted using either a scoring system or one based on professional judgement. Some firms adapted systems applied to design and product quality such as the Failure Mode and Effect Analysis (FMEA), used by Ford Motor Company, or the International Safety Rating System (ISRS), although this now has an accompanying environmental rating system.

The important issue for site management establishing their environmental effects register is that the methodology they use is logical and defendable as it is likely that the accredited environmental verifier will examine the systems in place used to determine 'significance' rather than the significance *per se*.

Most businesses will be able to determine the type and categories of environmental effects and the organizational areas and industrial activities that should be covered by the register. This information could then be compiled into two separate lists which would enable comparison to identify links between effect and activity or as input/output flow diagrams for each process. An example methodology is shown in Figure 3.4.

Figure 3.4 – *Environmental effects methodology*

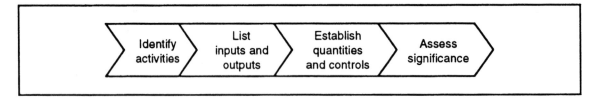

'Significance' is established using a mixture of objective and subjective factors and can be viewed as follows:

Significance = legislation + standards + stakeholders' views + scientific evidence + regulator's demands + public attitudes.

Significance needs to be determined and the following approaches illustrate some of the options available to management.

Option 1 – type of environmental effects are assessed for significance against a scale in Table 3.5.

Table 3.5 – *Environmental effects assessment significance scale*

Scale	Description	Criteria
1	Negligible	Very small effect. Low probability of occurrence.
2	Minor	Abnormal conditions would cause a breach of statutory regulations. Effect and probability of occurrence are both small.
3	Significant	The activity has an effect under normal operating conditions and results in a breach of statutory regulations under abnormal conditions. Effect and probability of occurrence are moderate.
4	Major	The activity under abnormal conditions is a major breach of statutory regulations. Effect, as a result of quantity and type of material, is extensive.

Option 2 – each environmental effect is assessed for significance against three ranked evaluation criteria in Table 3.6.

Table 3.6 – *Environmental effect assessment using risk*

Likelihood of occurrence		Likelihood of detection		Severity of consequence	
Criteria	Rank	Criteria	Rank	Criteria	Rank
Very high	5	Certain	0	None	0
High	4	Very high	1	Minor	2
Moderate	3	High	2	Low	4
Low	2	Moderate	3	Moderate	6
Very low	1	Low	4	High	8
None	0	Very low	5	Very high	10

Adding all three scores for each environmental effect would give a significance weighting with a high score being a significant environmental effect. Determining the background evidence for the criteria is difficult and will depend on legislation and standards, scientific knowledge, stakeholder influence etc. Combining the scores of 'likelihood of occurrence' and 'likelihood of detection' and plotting this for each environmental effect against 'severity of consequence' would represent this approach graphically.

No doubt many approaches will be used to establish significant environmental effects but all will contain objective and subjective elements. Sector-specific guidelines, which will be investigated by the Regulatory Committee, would assist management in this task.

Legislative register

A list of the legislative and regulatory requirements and procedures to maintain and update the register needs to be established for the environmental aspects of a company's activities, products and services. Basically, this refers to all the environmental legislation and standards that cover a particular site.

4. Operational control

It is necessary to identify activities and processes which do or could affect the environment. Once identified, controls and plans are required for the activities, the following criteria must be addressed:

- standard operating procedures for use by staff or contractors, especially where no instructions could lead to a breach of the environmental policy

- procurement procedures and procedures for contracted work so that they conform to the company's environmental policy

- monitoring and control of activities, environmental aspects, e.g. emissions to air, waste and effluent streams

- approval of planned processes and equipment

- written standards for performance.

Monitoring

Monitoring and associated records are required to determine whether the company environmental policy and site programme and management systems are being met.

Monitoring for each activity means the company must:

- identify and document required monitoring information

- define and document monitoring procedures

- establish and document acceptance criteria and actions in cases of unsatisfactory results

- assess and document the validity of previous monitoring information if systems malfunction.

Non-compliance and corrective action:

1. determine cause

2. draw up plan of action

3. initiate preventive actions corresponding to the level of risks

4. apply controls to ensure preventive actions are effective

5. record changes in procedures due to corrective action.

5. Environmental management documentation records

The environmental management system needs to be documented. These records are necessary not only to demonstrate compliance with the system but also to show how far the site's environmental objectives have been met.

Records are required to describe the following:

- the environmental policy, objectives and programme

- key roles and responsibilities

- the interactions of the system elements.

Figure 3.5 illustrates the various levels of documentation required in an environmental management system.

Figure 3.5 – Documentation hierarchy in an environmental management system

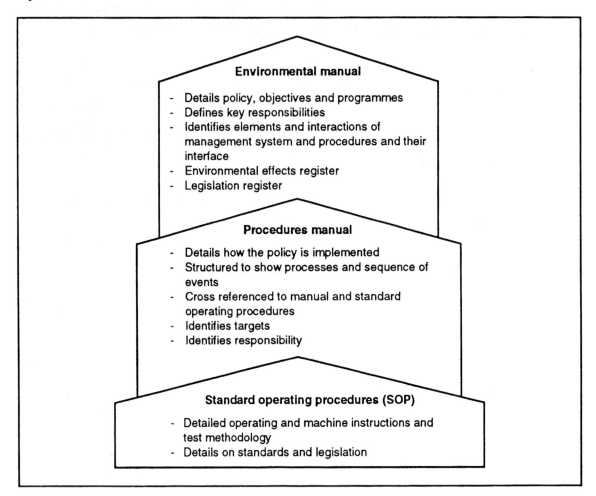

6. *Environmental audits*

Systematic and periodic reviews are required of the environmental management system to determine:

- whether environmental management activities are implemented effectively and conform to the environmental programme

- how effectively the environmental management system fulfils the company environmental policy.

These audits are a subset of the full environmental audit required under the scheme.

3.7   Establishing an environmental audit programme

An essential element of the Eco-management and audit scheme is the requirement to undertake environmental audits (Box 3 of Figure 3.1).

Environmental audit definition

A management tool comprising a systematic, documented, periodic and objective evaluation of the performance of the organization, management system and processes designed to protect the environment with the aim of:

(i)   facilitating management control of practices which may have impact on the environment;

(ii)   assessing compliance with company environmental policies.

Largely taken from the International Chamber of Commerce (ICC) definition of environmental auditing, this definition has the following important distinctions:

*   it is more precise and has a wider scope

*   it refers to protecting the environment rather than just 'helping to safeguard the environment'

*   it refers to management control of all practices rather than just environmental practices.

Key elements of environmental auditing as defined in the scheme:

*   auditing must be systematic, objective, periodic and documented

*   auditing evaluates performance of organizations, management systems and processes and must include the assessment of factual data to evaluate performance.

Environmental issues

The site environmental audit must address the same issues as the site's initial environmental review (see Section 3.4).

General guidelines

General reference is made to the international standard ISO 10011 part 1 (1990) *Guidelines for Auditing Quality Systems* (BS 7229). Environmental audits are to be conducted in line with ISO 10011, especially paragraphs:

- 4.2 on Roles and Responsibilities
- 5.1 on Auditing
- 5.2 on Preparing the Audit
- 5.3 on Executing the Audit
- 5.4.1 on Audit Report Preparation
- 5.4.2 on Report Content.

ISO 10011 is concerned with quality systems auditing; to make it applicable to environmental auditing the Regulation replaces particular words in the standard as shown in Table 3.7.

Table 3.7 – *ISO 10011 adapted for use in the Eco-management and audit scheme*

ISO 10011 terms	Regulation's replacement terms
quality system	environmental management system
quality standard	environmental standard
quality manual	environmental management manual
quality audit	environmental audit
client	the company's top management
auditee	the site

Staffing the environmental audit

The internal environmental audit of a site may be undertaken by a company's own trained personnel or an external consultant; however, company auditors should be independent of the audited activity to maintain objectivity. Auditors should not be seen as site police. Typically, audit teams are multidisciplinary and possess a mixture of technical, management and environmental legisiative skills.

Defining auditors' skills and making sure the consultant the company management may want to hire has the necessary experience and qualifications is difficult because there are no recognized standards for environmental auditors. A UK registration scheme for individual environmental auditors, administered by the Environmental Auditors Registration Association (EARA), will help to ensure standards amongst auditors. Three types of registration exist for individuals, depending on experience and qualifications: Associate Environmental Auditor; Environmental Auditor; and Principal Environmental Auditor.

In Denmark, the approach to registering environmental auditors is being tested on a company basis. Some UK consultancy firms have formed an Association of Environmental Consultants (AEC) which has established a Code of Practice on environmental management and environmental auditing for its members. This is intended to ensure a sound and effective framework for commissioning and undertaking environmental audits.

The accredited environmental verifier is **not** responsible for undertaking the internal environmental audit. However, it would be possible for a consultant to be both an auditor and an environmental verifier.

Cost of environmental audits

No cost estimates or limits for environmental auditing are identified in the Regulation. Some guidance on consultants fees for environmental auditing may be drawn from a recent survey of 300 consultants located in the UK, the Netherlands, Canada and USA undertaken by *Environment Risk* magazine. Respondents found it was difficult to estimate an average audit cost as the scope varied considerably between commissioning companies: 50% of all environmental audits cost between £5,000 and £10,000. Figure 3.6 shows graphically the charging rate for environmental audits undertaken by consultants.

Environmental audit methodology

Requirements for conducting environmental audits are outlined in Annex II of the Regulation and these follow closely the methodology in the International Chamber of Commerce's (ICC) book *Effective Environmental Auditing* and pioneered by the consultancy firm Arthur D. Little.

Annex II specifies:

1. Audit objectives.

2. Scope, organization and resources.

3. Planning and preparation for a site audit.

4. Audit activities.

5. Reporting audit findings and conclusions.

Figure 3.6 – Consultants' charges for environmental audits

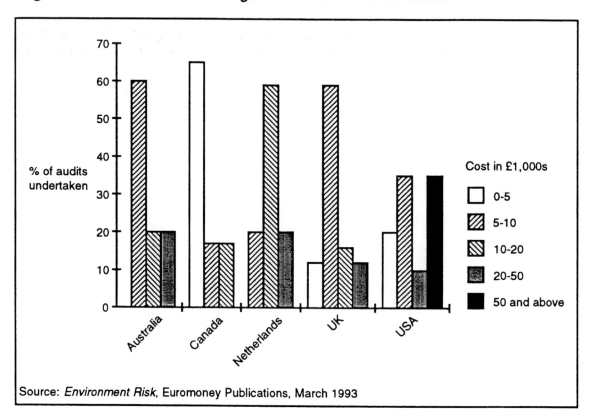

Source: *Environment Risk*, Euromoney Publications, March 1993

6.   Audit follow-up.

7.   Audit frequency.

1. Audit objectives

Site management may have various different objectives for their audit but under the scheme their objectives should include the following:

•   determine conformity with company policies and site programme

•   assess management systems

•   determine compliance with environmental regulatory requirements.

Objectives must be written for each audit or audit cycle and specify the audit frequency for each site activity.

2.i Audit scope

Audit scope needs to be defined for each audit or stage of an audit cycle. Scope must include assessment of the factual data necessary to evaluate performance.

Scope includes:

- subject areas covered

- activities to be audited

- environmental standards

- audit period.

2.ii Organization and resources

Auditor's Profile

- May be individuals or a team.

- Knowledge and experience of:

    (i)   sectors and fields being audited

    (ii)   environmental management

    (iii)   technical issues

    (iv)   environmental issues

    (v)   regulatory issues.

- Trained and proficient in auditing skills.

- Sufficiently independent of audited activities to be objective.

Top company management should support the audit and allocate sufficient resources and time to achieve its objectives and cover its scope.

3. Planning and preparation

Planning ensures each individual understands their role and responsibility and ensures appropriate resources are allocated.

Pre-audit activities will require the audit team to understand site activities and management systems and review previous audit findings or initial review findings.

4. On-site audit activities

On-site activities aim to evaluate environmental performance by determining whether or not sites meet applicable standards and site systems manage environmental responsibilities effectively and appropriately.

On-site activities:

* discussions with site personnel

* inspection of operating conditions and equipment

* review of records, written procedures and documents.

The audit methodology is shown in Figure 3.7. As can be seen from this figure, the scheme's audit steps are drawn from the Arthur D. Little approach to auditing.

5. Reporting audit findings and conclusions

The audit report must be written at the end of each audit or audit cycle by the auditors and be in such a form as to ensure full submission of the audit findings. Only one audit report is produced even if activities are audited at different times. Audit findings should be communicated to top company management.

The objectives of the audit report are to:

* Document audit scope.

* Provide management with information regarding degree of compliance with company environmental policy and the site's environmental progress.

* Provide management with information on the effectiveness and reliability of systems for monitoring site's environmental impact.

* Demonstrate the need, if necessary, for corrective action.

The audit report is not the environmental statement and does not have to be made public.

Figure 3.7 – *Environmental audit methodology of the Eco-management and audit scheme*

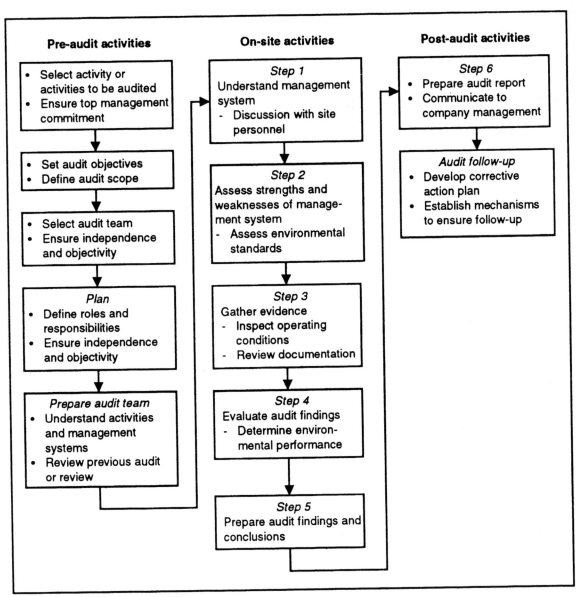

6. Audit follow-up

The audit is concluded by the development of an appropriate corrective action plan and mechanisms to ensure it is implemented.

A recent survey by the *Environment Risk* magazine identified that most consultants recommend follow-up procedures to environmental audits but checks to determine how these procedures are implemented are not regularly undertaken except in the USA. Figure 3.8 shows the country-wide pattern in graphical form.

Figure 3.8 – *Checks that environmental audit follow-up plans have been implemented*

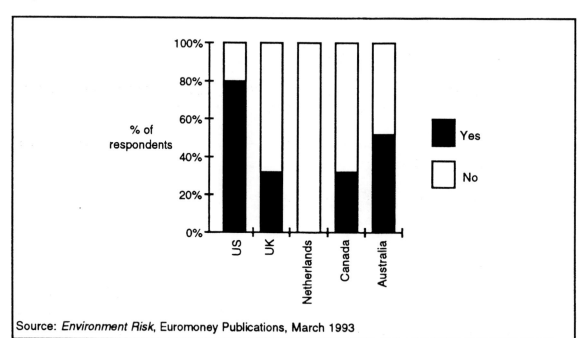

Source: *Environment Risk*, Euromoney Publications, March 1993

All sites registering on the Eco-management and audit scheme would have to implement environmental audit follow-up plans.

7. Audit frequency

Not all activities have to be audited at the same time or with the same frequency. An audit cycle can be established so a potentially more hazardous activity can be audited more often than other site activities as long as all the site's activities are audited within an interval of no longer than three years.

> Audit cycle definition
>
> The period of time in which all the activities in a given site are audited, according to the requirements of Article 4 and Annex II and on all the relevant environmental aspects mentioned in Annex I.C.

Top company management must establish audit frequency for each site activity with the help of guidelines established by the Commission under the Committee Procedure (see Section 5.7).

When establishing audit frequency for individual activities, top company management must take account of:

• potential overall environmental impact of the site's activities

- site's environmental programme.

Criteria for audit frequency for each activity:

- nature, scale and complexity of activity

- nature and scale of emission, waste, raw material and energy consumption and interaction with the environment

- importance and urgency of problems identified by the environmental review or previous audit

- history of environmental problems.

3.8 Preparing an environmental statement

Fundamental to the Eco-management and audit scheme, and the element which has been the most contentious with industry, is the public environmental statement and its validation by accredited environmental verifiers. Designed to provide the scheme with credibility in the eyes of the public, the environmental statement should be a full and fair reflection of a site's environmental performance and progress.

A site's first environmental statement will be prepared after the initial environmental review and the establishment of the site's environmental programme and management system. Subsequent environmental statements will be produced after each environmental audit or audit cycle of the site's activities.

Two important factors must be considered when preparing a site's environmental statement:

1. It must be designed for public consumption and therefore written in a concise and comprehensible form. Technical material may be appended.

2. Except for the first statement produced from the initial environmental review, each subsequent statement needs to highlight changes since the last statement.

The format of a site's environmental statement has not been specified in the Regulation nor does the scheme indicate who should prepare the statement but minimum contents are specified.

Minimum content for an environmental statement:

- A description of the site's activities.

- An assessment of all the significant environmental issues related to site activities.

- A summary of figures on pollution emissions, waste production, consumption of raw material, energy and water, noise and any other significant environmental aspects.

- Other environmental performance factors.

- A presentation of the company's environmental policy and the site's programme and management system.

- The deadline for the next statement.

- The name of the accredited environmental verifier that validated the statement.

- Identification of significant changes since the previous statement.

Few examples exist of independently verified environmental statements. Of the 17 companies involved in the Eco-management and audit scheme pilot project at the time of publication, none so far has presented a validated environmental statement: only Hydro Aluminium Metals was in the process of publication. Building on the success of its first environmental statement, in 1993 The Body Shop International independently published an environmental statement, *The Green Book 2*, in line with the Regulation's requirements and had it and the company's internal systems independently verified by the consultancy firm ERM.

Annual simplified statements

Participating sites will have to produce simplified annual statements in intervening years between full environmental statements, except under two conditions:

- where there have been few significant changes at the site since the last statement

- or where the accredited environmental verifier considers the nature and scale of the activities at the site are such that no statement is necessary until the completion of the next audit or audit cycle.

The contents of the simplified annual statement will be based on the list of minimum contents for the full environmental statement.

Simplified statements will not be required to be validated annually but will undergo validation at the same time that the full environmental statement is validated by the accredited environmental verifier. If, in practice, the validation of simplified statements proves difficult to implement, this provision of the Regulation will be reviewed by the Council and the Commission and could be removed.

Who is the public?

A difficult issue for company management preparing a site's public environmental statement is deciding who is 'the public'? Nowhere in the Regulation is 'the public' defined. It could be the general public, but then again 'the public' could also be the local community, shareholders, banks, insurance companies, regulators or the media. The list is potentially endless but it is clear that 'the public' is made up of different segments (see the pie chart in Figure 3.9) which have different needs and expectations of an environmental statement.

Figure 3.9 – *Pie chart showing the many segments of 'the public'*

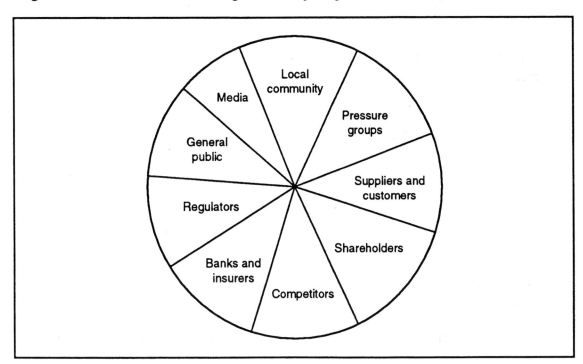

There is only one environmental statement to communicate the site's environmental progress to all the various segments of 'the public'; therefore, defining the target audience for the environmental statement is very important. Consequently, certain crucial conditions need to be fulfilled when preparing a site's environmental statement. A statement must be:

- clear and honest

- have top management commitment

- well produced (this does not mean lots of glossy, pretty pictures)

Currently, much of industry feels battle weary. Painted as the cause of all evil by certain sections of society, the majority appear to have reacted by battening down the hatches and waiting for the storm to blow over. This reactionary response will not work. The demands of the public for more environmental information will not go away and this is where the environmental statement of the Eco-management and audit scheme offers management an opportunity to break the cycle of mistrust (Figure 3.10). The environmental statement is a means to adopt a frank and open dialogue with the public but in a structured and credible way, yet under the clear control of company management.

Figure 3.10 – *Cycle of mistrust*

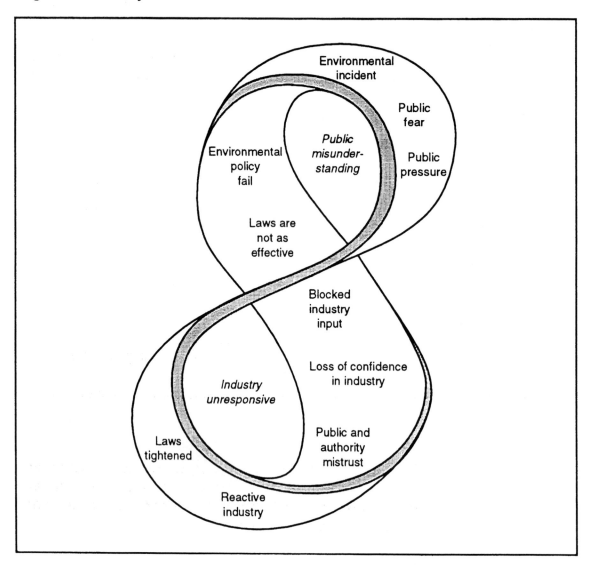

CHAPTER 4

VALIDATION AND THE ACCREDITED ENVIRONMENTAL VERIFIERS

To make the Eco-management and audit scheme a credible market-based tool, it was necessary to build into the scheme an independent third party checking process which could guarantee the quality of information put into the public domain. The new profession of accredited environmental verifiers will be developed for the role.

4.1 Who are accredited environmental verifiers?

Accredited environmental verifiers can either be an organization or, with limited accreditation scope, individuals. They do not replace the Member States' environmental regulatory authorities such as HMIP or NRA. Environmental verifiers can operate in any EC Member State irrespective of where they were accredited. If, however, they undertake validation activities in another EC country they must notify, and be supervised by, that country's accreditation organization. Details on the accreditation of environmental verifiers and their functions are outlined in Annex III of the Regulation.

Accreditation criteria for organisations

Personnel

- The environmental verifier must be competent for the accredited scope and have personnel which are qualified, trained and experienced in the following:

  (i)   environmental auditing methodologies
  (ii)   management information systems and processes
  (iii)   environmental issues
  (iv)   relevant legislation and standards
  (v)   guidance information on the Regulation
  (vi)   relevant technical knowledge of the activities being verified.

- Records must be kept on staff training, experience and qualifications.

Independence and objectivity

- A verifier must be independent, impartial and be able to demonstrate that its organization and personnel are free from any commercial, financial or other pressure which might influence its verification activities and judgement or endanger its trust.

- Verifiers complying with the European standard EN 45012 *General Criteria for Certification Bodies Operating Quality Systems Certification* (BS 7512) Section 4 on *Administrative Structure* and Section 5 on *Terms of Reference of Governing Bodies* will have met the independence and objectivity criteria.

Procedures

- Procedures and methodologies must be documented and exist for:

  (i)   verification requirements under the scheme
  (ii)   quality control mechanisms
  (iii) confidentiality provisions.

Organization

A verifier must have:

- An organizational chart detailing structures and responsibilities in its organization and make it available upon request.

- A statement of legal status, ownership and funding sources.

Accreditation criteria for individuals

- Accreditation will be limited in scope to those activities where the individual can demonstrate all the competencies and experience to allow the accreditation body to determine accreditation.

- Individuals must demonstrate, for their accreditation, scope, competence and expertise in the following:

  (i)   technical issues
  (ii)   environmental issues
  (iii) regulatory issues
  (iv)   verification methods and procedures.

- Individuals must meet the same criteria for independence and objectivity and procedures as an organization seeking accreditation (see above).

All accredited environmental verifiers must inform the accreditation body of any changes which could alter their accreditation or scope.

Validation is described as essentially a private sector function but as the Eco-management and audit scheme extends to the public sector there may be a place for public sector organizations taking on the role of accredited environmental verifier. There is nothing in the Regulation which precludes public sector organizations from doing this.

4.2 Who accredits and supervises environmental verifiers?

Member States are required to establish a system, ensuring appropriate consultation with interested parties, for the accreditation and supervision of environmental verifiers within 21 months of the Regulation entering into force, i.e., by April 1995. Existing accreditation institutions, the competent body or another appropriate body, may be used for the function.

A consultation document has been prepared jointly by the UK Department of the Environment and the Department of Trade and Industry on the various options available for establishing the UK accreditation system and the possible bodies which could be responsible for running such a system. This document also addresses accreditation of certification bodies for BS 7750 and was made available for public comment in July 1993. Copies can be obtained from either department.

The National Accreditation Council for Certification Bodies (NACCB) is the favoured option for both accrediting organizations to undertake certification to BS 7750 and accrediting environmental verifiers. Doubt exists, however, about NACCB's qualifications to assess environmental credentials necessary for BS 7750 certifications and Eco-management and audit scheme verifications. The government's consultation document suggests that NACCB will require additional expertise to undertake its new responsibilities and will need to take into account criticisms levelled at the costs and burdens it placed on small and medium-sized enterprises under the certification schemes for BS 5750, the quality systems standard.

Within a three-year cycle, the accreditation body must regularly review accredited environmental verifiers to make sure they comply with all the accreditation requirements and to ensure the quality of their verifications. Termination or suspension of an environmental verifier's accreditation or alteration to the verifier's accreditation scope is possible, but this may only be done after the verifier has been given the opportunity of a hearing.

The Commission will facilitate collaboration between the Member States via the Committee Procedure (see Section 5.7) to ensure consistency in the systems across the EC and to assist the supervision of verifier's activities in the Member States.

4.3 Applying to become an accredited environmental verifier

Environmental verifiers will need to be certain that they satisfy all the accreditation criteria before applying for accreditation. An official application form, which has not yet been developed in the UK, will require the following information:

Official application form for accreditation

The applicant is required to:

- declare knowledge of the functioning of the accreditation system

- agree to fulfil the accreditation procedure

- agree to pay the appropriate accreditation fees

- agree to comply with accreditation criteria

- divulge previous applications and accreditations.

The accreditation body will provide applicants with the following documentation, which details:

- accreditation procedures

- rights and duties of accredited environmental verifiers

- fees

- additional relevant information if requested.

4.4 Accreditation process

The accreditation body will follow four accreditation steps when assessing the application of an environmental verifier for accreditation.

Step 1 – Gathering information

Information will be gathered to allow the accreditation body to evaluate the applicant. The information required is as follows:

- General applicant information:

  - name and address
  - legal status
  - human resources
  - relationship with larger corporate entity.

- Information to assess applicant's compliance with accreditation criteria (see Section 4.1).

- Information to establish the scope and possible limitation of accreditation activities of the applicant.

Step 2 – Assessment

The information supplied by the applicant is reviewed and assessed to determine a view on whether the applicant meets the accreditation criteria. Establishing the view of the verifier can include assessing relevant work as well as making additional enquiries and, if necessary, interviewing environmental verifier personnel.

The review is undertaken by the staff of the accreditation body or by representatives appointed by the accreditation body. In both cases, applicants should be informed of the review and be able to comment on its contents.

Step 3 – Review

The accreditation body reviews all the material necessary to determine an accreditation.

Step 4 – Decision

A decision is made and documented by the accreditation body to grant or refuse accreditation on the basis of the review in Step 2. Accreditation may come with limitations in scope but always with terms and conditions.

Accredited environmental verifiers may want to extend the scope of their accreditation and the accreditation body must have written details on how they go about obtaining an extension.

4.5 Role of the accredited environmental verifier

Accredited environmental verifiers have two clear roles (Boxes 5a and 5b in Figure 4.1).

1.   To examine the elements of the Eco-management and audit scheme at the site to verify that they meet the requirements of the Regulation (Box 5a).

2.   To validate the site's environmental statement (Box 5b).

Figure 4.1 – Accredited environmental verifier's role

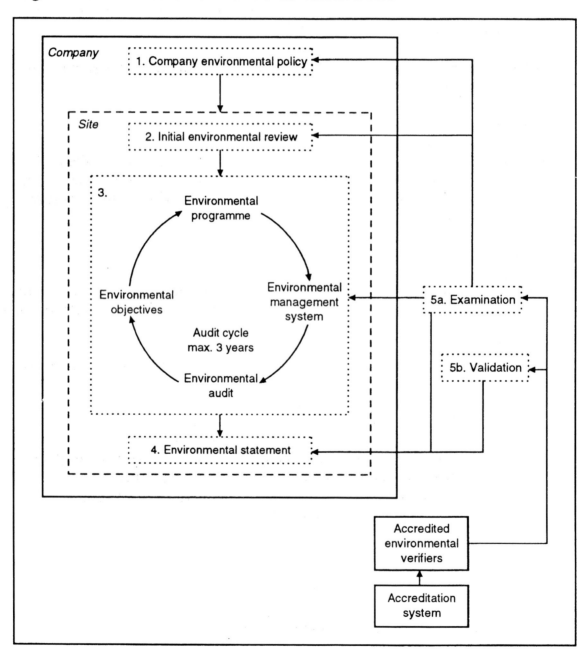

Examination

The accredited environmental verifier has to examine the following for conformity with the Regulation:

- environmental policies
- environmental programmes
- environmental management systems
- environmental review and audit procedures
- environmental statement.

In addition, the accredited environmental verifier will check the functioning of the environmental management system and investigate the technical validity of the environmental review and audits.

During the investigation the verifier should not duplicate the review or audit process.

Validation

As well as checking the reliability and coverage of the data and information in the environmental statement, the verifier will also have to validate that information and check that all the significant environmental issues of relevance to the site have been included in the statement.

Verification methodology

Little detail is specified in the Eco-management and audit scheme on how accredited environmental verifiers will execute their duties but they will include:

- Examination of documents on site and before the site visit, and these include:

    (i)   information on the site and its activities
    (ii)   the environmental policy and programme
    (iii)   a description of the site's environmental management system
    (iv)   previous site environmental review or audit details
    (v)   corrective action details as a result of the review or audit
    (vi)   draft environmental statement

- A site visit

- Interviews with site personnel

- Preparation of a report for company management

- Solution of the issues raised in the report.

The accredited environmental verifier does not have the power to interfere with company policies, to adjust a site's environmental objectives or to suggest solutions to issues for which they are not competent.

Accredited environmental verifier's report

After completing their examination and validation activities, the accredited environmental verifier will produce a report to company management which will cover three specific areas:

1. Cases of non-compliance with the Eco-management and audit scheme.

2. Any technical defects identified in the environmental review, the audit or the environmental management system.

3. Points of disagreement with the site's draft environmental statement including any additional details or amendments that the verifier has identified.

Uncertainty about the verification activities of accredited environmental verifiers prompted a joint study between the UK Department of the Environment, the Commission and a consultancy firm called Environmental Resources Limited. This study sought to identify how environmental verifiers would go about their verification duties. In part, it was recognized that verification activities will involve professional judgement. The final results of the study were produced in July 1993. The draft document will be communicated to interested parties such as trade associations and the Member States and may be produced as guidelines for verifiers via the Regulatory Committee.

4.6 Accredited environmental verifier's relationship with the company

At all times during their accreditation activities, the accredited environmental verifier must operate in a sound and professional manner. The verifier will operate on the basis of a written agreement with the company. The contract will define the verifier's scope of work and will not only enable the verifier to operate in an independent and professional manner but also commits the company to providing the necessary co-operation.

A number of companies have already employed external consultants to act as third party verifiers of their environmental practices and performance, attaching verification statements to the company's environmental reports. Norsk Hydro

(UK) Ltd. employed Lloyd's Register in 1990 to perform a third party assessment and this is published in Norsk Hydro's first environmental report. The Body Shop International has produced two *Green Books* on its environmental performance, both of which have had verification statements appended to them. Arthur D. Little undertook an assessment of the Body Shop's environmental review of its headquarters and manufacturing site in Watersmead, UK, in 1992 and this year ERM has verified the *Green Book 2* using criteria it has developed to match the statement to Eco-management and audit scheme requirements.

4.7   Test cases

Three different implementation cases and appropriate accredited environmental verifier actions are outlined in the Regulation.

Case 1 – Verifier validates statement

A site had all the elements of the Eco-management and audit scheme in place and functioning and the statement is accurate and sufficiently detailed.

Action: the accredited environmental verifier will validate the site's environmental statement.

Case 2 – Statement needs revision

A site has every element of the Eco-management and audit scheme in place and functioning but there is a problem with the environmental statement. Either the statement needs to be revised or is incomplete or the annual statements for intervening years are incorrect, misleading or absent.

Action: the accredited environmental verifier will discuss the necessary changes with company management and will not validate the environmental statement until all corrections have been undertaken.

Case 3 – Improvements are recommended

The site has applied one or more of the elements of the Eco-management and audit scheme unsatisfactorily or they are technically incorrect.

Action: appropriate recommendations for improvements will be made by the accredited environmental verifier to company management. The site's environmental statement will not be validated until all shortcomings in the scheme's application have been addressed and the environmental statement revised to meet the new situation.

CHAPTER 5

ORGANIZATIONS AND REGISTRATION

Figure 5.1 illustrates all the organizations involved in, and registration under, the Eco-management and audit scheme.

Figure 5.1 – Organizations involved in, and registration under, the Eco-management and audit scheme

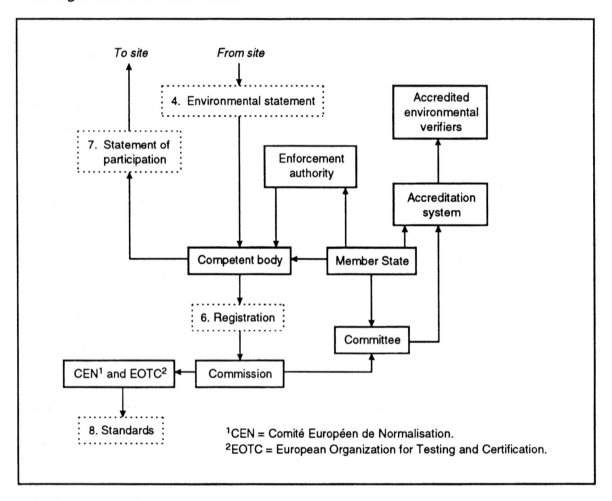

5.1   Member State's functions and fees

Under the Regulation, the 12 Member States of the EC have responsibilities for information, infringements and competent bodies. Member States may also establish a system of fees to cover the promotional cost of the scheme as well as the administrative costs of site registration and accreditation of environmental verifiers. No charges have yet been established by the UK government.

Each Member State has the responsibility to:

*   Inform companies of the contents of the Regulation and the public of the objectives and principles of the scheme.

*   Take appropriate legal or administrative measures in case of non-compliance with the Regulation's provisions.

*   Designate an independent and neutral competent body within 12 months of the Regulation entering into force, i.e., by July 1994.

5.2 Dealings with the competent body – what is it and what does it do?

A company wanting to register a site on the Eco-management and audit scheme will have to deal directly with the competent body (shown in Figure 5.1), submitting to it an application (see Section 5.3) which must include a validated environmental statement and a fee (not yet established). The competent body will directly inform site management if the site is successfully registered on the scheme and place it on the register. It will also inform any site which is de-registered.

What is the competent body?

Each Member State is required to designate within 12 months of the Regulation entering into force, i.e., by July 1994, a competent body which must be independent, neutral, consistent in its duties and have procedures for considering interested parties' observations about registered sites.

The competent body can either be an existing body such as NACCB or a new non-departmental public body such as the organization established for the Eco-labelling Regulation. There is nothing to prevent a Member State from selecting a private organization as long as it could guarantee its independence and neutrality.

In July 1993, the UK's Department of Trade and Industry and the Department of the Environment released a consultation document on the available options for the UK competent body. All public comments were to be made by September 10, 1993. The UK government's preferred option is to widen the remit of the UK Eco-labelling Board, which is the competent body for the EC Eco-labelling scheme, to make it the competent body for the Eco-management and audit scheme as well.

What does the competent body do?

The competent body has two clear functions:

1.   Registering/de-registering sites in the Eco-management and audit scheme and communicating this information to site management.

2.   Keeping the list of registered sites and sending it annually, either directly or indirectly, by a national authority, to the Commission.

Depending on the Member State, the competent body could also be responsible for the accreditation of environmental verifiers (see Section 4.2). This option is not favoured by the UK government. The competent body can charge fees to cover the administrative costs of site registration procedures.

The competent body is not designed to be another national environmental inspection agency like HMIP; however, it is responsible for policing the way in which companies publicise their participation in the scheme and use the statement of participation. It is not required to undertake any physical inspection of the sites registered or requesting registration in the Eco-management and audit scheme.

Member States are responsible for promoting the scheme to industry and the public. Although not specifically assigned to the competent body, the UK government suggests that this responsibility should be undertaken by the competent body.

5.3   Registration and de-registration procedures for companies

Site registration and de-registration on the Eco-management and audit scheme is controlled by the competent body. Registration (Box 6 in Figure 5.1) only occurs once all the relevant information has been submitted to the competent body and the competent body is satisfied the site meets all the Regulation's requirements, including complying with all relevant environmental legislation. No site inspection is undertaken.

Application for site registration

A company needs to submit to the competent body the following in its application for initial and subsequent site registration:

•   The site's validated environmental statement.

•   A registration fee (not yet established).

- Information on the company and site outlined in Annex V of the Regulation which includes the following:

  (i)   name of company
  (ii)   name and location of the site
  (iii)   brief description of the activities at the site (this information can be appended)
  (iv)   name and address of the accredited environmental verifier who validated the site's environmental statement (statement should be appended)
  (v)   deadline for submission of the next validated environmental statement
  (vi)   a brief description of the environmental management system
  (vii)   a description of the auditing programme established for the site
  (viii) the site's validated environmental statement.

De-registration of a site

The competent body has the power to de-register sites. De-registered sites are deleted from the Eco-management and audit scheme register and the site management informed by the competent body.

De-registration can occur in three ways.

1.   If a company fails to submit a validated environmental statement for a site and registration fee within three months of the deadline specified in the site's previous statement.

2.   If a competent body becomes aware that the site is no longer in compliance with the requirements of the Regulation. (This could possibly be by receiving information from interested parties.)

3.   If an enforcement authority such as HMIP or NRA informs the competent body that the site is no longer in compliance with relevant environmental legislation, the site will be refused registration or have its registration suspended. Suspension or refusal of registration will only be reversed once the competent body has been assured by the enforcement authority that the site has rectified the breach and has procedures in place to ensure it does not re-occur.

5.4 Registration number and list of sites

Once the competent body is satisfied with the site's application for registration on the Eco-management and audit scheme, it gives the site a registration number and informs site management that its site appears on the register of Eco-management and audit scheme sites. Each year the lists of registered sites in the 12 Member States will be communicated to the Commission (shown in Figure 5.1) and a complete list published in the EC's *Official Journal.*

5.5 Cost of registration

Member States may set up a system of fees to cover the costs of site registration procedures. At this stage the UK government has not set any charges but any fee scale must take into account the need not to out-price company participation in the Eco-management and audit scheme, especially of small and medium-sized enterprises.

5.6 Relationship with enforcement authorities

Companies registered on the Eco-management and audit scheme will still be subjected to the same inspection formalities by the enforcement authorities such as HMIP, NRA and the local authorities. Nevertheless, a site operating the scheme will be more likely to demonstrate its effective compliance with legislation and build trust with the authorities, thus relieving the burden of monitoring and enforcement action from the regulating authority, and allowing it to concentrate on more lax sites.

Industries covered by integrated pollution control (IPC) have to use the Best Available Techniques Not Entailing Excessive Cost (BATNEEC). The Eco-management and audit scheme could assist management in gaining authorization of its prescribed processes.

Enforcement authorities have the power to inform the competent body of a site's breaches of environmental legislation and prevent its registration to – or get it suspended from – the scheme. The site will not be registered or reinstated until the competent body receives satisfactory assurance from the enforcement authority that the site has rectified the breach and has put in place arrangements to prevent the breach re-occurring.

5.7 Role of the European Commission

Committee procedure

Under Article 19 of the Regulation, a Regulatory Committee is required to assist the Commission during the first five years of the scheme's operation. The committee will consist of representatives from the 12 Member States, usually national experts from their Departments of Environment, and be chaired by the Commission.

The Regulatory Committee has several functions:

- It will have the power to adapt any part of the five Annexes in light of experience gained during the Regulation's initial operation and before the review date of July 1998. This could include suggesting the development of sector application guides.

- It will have the power to recognize national and international standards as fulfilling certain aspects of the scheme.

- It will eventually develop guidelines for environmental verifiers and accreditation organizations.

The Regulatory Committee has an important role. It can change the details of information concerning environmental policies, programmes, management systems, auditing and accreditation of environmental verifiers and their functions before the review date of July 1998 and without going through the long-drawn-out procedures of a legislative review.

Commission proposals

Under the Regulation, the Commission is required to make a number of proposals to the Council which will assist the application of the Eco-management and audit scheme.

Proposals

1. To encourage greater participation by small and medium-sized enterprises (SMEs).

2. Concerning how SMEs might be assisted in their internal environmental audit and the verification procedures.

The Commission has also requested appropriate European standardization bodies to develop a European environmental management system standard and procedures for certification (see Section 6.5).

CHAPTER 6

LINKS WITH NATIONAL, EUROPEAN AND INTERNATIONAL STANDARDS

6.1   Using standards

Companies implementing and being certified to relevant national, European or international standards, such as an environmental management system standard, will have met those specific parts of the Regulation. This is as long as the standard they use fulfils two conditions:

1.   The standard must be submitted to and recognized by the Commission.

2.   Certification to the standard is essential and must be undertaken by a body whose accreditation is recognized by the Member State where the site is located.

The British Standards Institution (BSI) is considering submitting its environmental management systems standard (BS 7750) to the Commission for recognition. BSI should be confident that its standard will meet Commission approval since much of Annex I of the Regulation, which details environmental management systems, looks remarkably similar to the standard.

6.2   Benefits of using BS 7750

There are two benefits of using BS 7750. Firstly, organizations currently implementing BS 7750 are meeting the environmental management system's part of the Eco-management and audit scheme and secondly, verification activities undertaken by the accredited environmental verifier may be reduced.

On the second point: when BS 7750 is recognized by the Commission, organizations implementing and being certified to the standard will achieve a significant benefit when it comes to the verification requirements under the Eco-management and audit scheme.

Normal verification activities undertaken by the accredited environmental verifier are both an examination of the scheme's elements at the site and the validation of the site's environmental statement. If, however, a site has been certified to BS 7750, the verifier will not duplicate the examination process but will accept the site's certification certificate as proof of third party verification. This should result in a cost saving to the site. Organizations with a corporate culture of using standards and those enterprises currently implementing BS 7750 should be heartened by this news.

6.3 Links with BS 7750

BS 7750 is compatible with and can be used as a sub-set of the Eco-management and audit scheme. Two factors ensure that BS 7750 could be used to satisfy the environmental management system's component of the scheme (Box 3 Figure 3.1). Firstly, much of what is specified as an environmental management system in the Eco-management and audit scheme is BS 7750. And secondly, BSI is currently reviewing BS 7750 in light of the pilot project but, more importantly, in light of changes to the Eco-management and audit scheme. This review will bring the standard even closer to fulfilling the Regulation's requirements

Original comparisons by BSI between BS 7750 and the scheme were made on a very early version of the draft Regulation (December 1991, version 3) when it was still referred to as the Eco-audit scheme. Table 6.1 highlights the difference between the specifications of BS 7750 and the requirements of the Eco-management and audit Regulation.

Table 6.1 – *Differences between the Eco-management and audit scheme and BS 7750*

Requirements of the Eco-management and audit scheme	Requirements of BS 7750
A piece of EC legislation	A national standard
Applies across the whole of the EC	Applies in the UK
Applies to sites	Can apply to the whole organization
Restricted to industrial activities	Open to any sector or activity
Non-industrial activities can only be included on an experimental basis	Open to non-industrial activities, e.g. transport and local government
Focuses on environmental improvement and associated results at a site and the provision of information to the public	Focuses on organizations' implementing systems; environmental improvements emerge from the system
Initial environmental review essential and assessable	Preparatory environmental review advisable but not a specification of the standard
Environmental policy commitment to continuous improvement of environmental performance and compliance with relevant environmental legislation	Environmental policy commitment to continual improvement of environmental performance, no reference to legislation in the standard's specifications

Table 6.1 – continued

Environmental audit assess the performance of organization management systems, processes and factual data	Environmental management audits concerned with the assessment of environmental management systems, its operation and results only
Maximum audit or audit cycle frequency specified at three years	Frequency of audits not specified
A presentation of the environmental policy, programme and management system made publicly available in the statement	Only environmental policy must be publicly available
Public environmental statement and annual simplified statement including factual data on environmental performance essential	Not required, left up to management as to how much information to disclose
Third party verification essential	Third party certification optional
Verification duties detailed and systems specified for who conducts verifications and supervises these activities	Certification details not specified
Means of advertising site participation specified by Statement of Participation	Advertising not specified
Government assigned national competent body controls registration of sites	No national registration body

Companies currently piloting BS 7750 can be pleased with their efforts because much of BS 7750 appears in the Regulation, as can been seen from Table 6.2 (the comparison is made on the proposed revised text of BS 7750 Doc. ref. DC 93/400220).

Whether or not management decides to apply for BS 7750, the Eco-management and audit scheme or both (or neither) will depend on the organization's corporate culture, its market exposure in Europe and the perceived benefits it can derive from registration. Companies with sites located in more than one EC country would be able to promote their achievements more comprehensively with the Eco-management and audit scheme. Registration, however, is not possible until April 1995. BS 7750 could prove to be a useful means of testing the water and a stepping stone to achieving the EC scheme.

Table 6.2 – *Comparison between BS 7750 and the Eco-management and audit scheme*

Requirements of Regulation Articles and Annexes	Environmental management system 4.1	Environmental policy 4.2	Organization and personnel 4.3	Environmental effects 4.4	Environmental objectives and targets 4.5	Environmental management programme 4.6	Management manual and documentation 4.7	Operational control 4.8	Environmental management records 4.9	Environmental management audits 4.10	Environmental management reviews 4.11
Environmental Policy Anx. I.A.1.2.3, I.B.1, I.C and I.D		•									
Environmental Objectives Anx. I.A.4 and I.B.1					•						
Environmental Programme Anx. I.A.5, I.B.1 and I.C						•					
Environmental Management System Anx. I.B	•										
Organization and Personnel Anx. I.B.2			•	•							
Environmental Effects Anx. I.B.3				•							
Operational Control Anx. I.B.4								•			
Management Records Anx. I.B.5							•		•		
Management Audits Anx. I.B.6										•	•
Environmental Review Anx.I.C											
Environmental Audit Anx. I.C and II											
Environmental Statement Art. 5 and Anx. V											
Validation Art. 4 and Anx. III											

A cell containing a • denotes a close similarity in the words used in the Regulation and those used in BS 7750.

6.4 BS 7750: the new version

BS 7750 was published as a standard and became effective on March 16, 1992 with the provision that it would be reviewed in light of the BS 7750 pilot project and changes to the Eco-management and audit Regulation. Implementing organizations in the BS 7750 pilot project had reported back to BSI through their individual working groups by April 19, 1993.

The BSI environmental management standard sub-committee ESS1/1 has reviewed the standard. A draft for public comment (Doc. ref. DC 93/400220) of the revised standard was released for public comment in July 1993. Two months is allowed for public comment until August 31, 1993. All submitted views will be considered by BSI's technical committee ESS1. A final revised standard is expected for publication at the end of January 1994. It is this revised version of BS 7750 that will be submitted to the European Commission for recognition.

6.5 Mandate for a European environmental management systems standard

The Commission has requested Comité Européen de Normalization (CEN) to develop and adopt a standard for environmental management systems for use with the Eco-management and audit scheme and the appropriate European certification body, European Organization for Testing and Certification (EOTC), to develop guidelines for environmental management and auditing certification.

Both organizations have to base their developments on the requirements for environmental policies, programmes, management systems and environmental auditing outlined in Annexes I and II of the Regulation. They must also take into account the objectives, principles and provisions of the Eco-management and audit scheme. This means that any European environmental management standard will look very similar to BS 7750 because Annex I, which deals with environmental management systems, looks very similar to the standard (see Table 6.2).

CEN, which includes both EC and EFTA countries, has delegated its responsibility to develop an environmental management systems standard to the International Standards Organization (ISO), believing that it is better to have one international standard developed rather than a number of regional standards. ISO began its preparatory work in 1992 by establishing the Strategic Advisory Group on the Environment (SAGE) to investigate the possibility of developing environmental standards. The SAGE working group, which investigated environmental management systems, was chaired by the UK.

ISO is notoriously slow at developing standards – the quality standard ISO 9000 (BS 5750) took around seven years before it was published as a standard. However, efforts are being made to speed up the standard-making process which should normally take only three years; approval time for the standard will be halved from six to three months. In mid 1993, ISO set up a technical committee supported by six sub-committees to look at environmental standards. Sub committee 1, whose chair and secretariat are British, will investigate environmental management systems.

ISO has just 21 months to develop an environmental management systems standard if it is going to be in time for the launch of the Eco-management and audit scheme. Issues are further complicated by the fact that the Commission has mandated CEN, not ISO, to develop the standard. The Commission has no direct relationship with ISO. If ISO does not meet the deadline for producing an environmental management systems standard, CEN does have the procedures to adopt an interim standard to fulfil its mandate. CEN could draw on the available standards in Europe which currently include BS 7750 and the French experimental environmental management systems standard or the model for environmental management systems developed by the SAGE working group.

CHAPTER 7

BENEFITS AND PITFALLS OF THE ECO-MANAGEMENT AND AUDIT SCHEME

7.1 Overview of the benefits and pitfalls

Before embarking on the Eco-management and audit scheme, company management would want to identify the type of benefits they could expect to derive from registering one or more sites on the scheme and any potential pitfalls. The following list of benefits and pitfalls is drawn from the expected outcome of participation and some actual issues identified during the scheme's pilot programme.

Benefits

- Scheme's statement of participation.

- Improved environmental performance and reduction in environmental impact, e.g. waste reduction.

- Competitive advantage.

- Improved public relations and alleviation of public fears regarding operations.

- Marketing tool.

- Improved relations with regulators making it easier to obtain licences or planning permission.

- Identification of cost savings.

- Increased profile within corporate body, making it easier to obtain finance for capital expenditure.

- Useful in formalizing and co-ordinating existing systems and ensuring company personnel are working to approved methods concerning environmental issues.

- Fulfilment of group environmental policy.

- Mechanism for controlling environmental legislation requirements and enabling management to stay ahead of legislation.

- Motivating employees, improving staff morale and raising staff awareness of environmental issues and responsibilities.

- Better way of getting more information to the public.

- Enabling site to meet moral obligations.

- Providing assurance to senior management.

- Raising the prominence of environmental issues within the company.

- Better relationships with local community.

- Cheaper insurance premiums.

- Proactive approach.

Pitfalls

- Exposing environmental liabilities (could also be a benefit).

- Uncontrolled environmental information.

- Long-term resource commitments.

- Cost of implementation and verification.

- Increasing some staff's work load.

7.2 Statement of participation

Competent bodies reward successfully registered sites with a statement of participation (Box 7 Figure 5.1). Companies may use this statement of participation to publicize and promote their involvement in the scheme, putting it on company environmental statements, brochures, reports, headed paper and company advertisements. Restrictions of use do exist, however, and the means by which a site promotes its inclusion in the scheme will be controlled by the competent body.

Four different versions of the statement of participation are included in Annex IV of the Regulation, shown here in Figure 7.1. In each of the four statements, the graphic symbol remains unchanged, but each describes different registration possibilities. Depending on the number and geographical location of the registered site/s, different statements of participation will be applicable.

Figure 7.1 – Statements of participation

This site has an environmental management system and its environmental performance is reported to the public in accordance with the Community eco-management and audit scheme. (Registration No...)

Author's comment: Statement one is for single site registration. The site's registration number must be included.

All the sites in the Community where we carry out our industrial activities have an environmental management system and their environmental performance is reported on to the public in accordance with the Community eco-management and audit scheme. (Plus optional statement regarding practices in third countries.)

Author's comment: Statement two is for multisite registration covering all EC countries, neither names and registration numbers nor countries need to be listed. This statement has an interesting addition as the activities of non-EC located sites may be mentioned.

All the sites in [name(s) of the Community Member State(s)] where we carry out our industrial activities have an environmental management system and their environmental performance is reported on to the public in accordance with the Community eco-management and audit scheme.

Author's comment: Statement three is for multisite registration located in a number but not all of the EC countries. Site names do not have to be listed but applicable countries need to be cited.

The following sites where we carry out our industrial activities have an environmental management system and their environmental performance is reported on to the public in accordance with the Community eco-management and audit scheme:
- site name, registration number
-
- ...

Author's comment: Statement four is for multisites registration in one country. All their names and registration numbers must be listed.

Restriction of use

The statement of participation may not be used in product advertising or on products or their packaging. The graphic symbol may not be used on its own without the statement. The Regulation's Article 16 on infringements allows Member States to take legal or administrative actions in cases of non-compliance with the Regulation, e.g. misuse of the statement of participation.

7.3   Improving environmental performance

Essentially a fitness programme for sites, the rigours of the Eco-management and audit scheme will identify and assist company management improvements of environmental performance. From focusing on environmental performance, potential spin-off benefits will arise such as cost savings through more efficient use of resources and more effective minimization of waste.

Another attractive benefit linked to improved environmental performance is site management ability to demonstrate to the regulators such as Her Majesty's Inspectorate of Pollution and the National Rivers Authority that its operations are effectively managed. Regulators have limited resources; consequently, an industrial site applying the scheme could relieve the burden of monitoring, allowing enforcement action to be concentrated on more lax sites. Registration on the scheme may also help in an application for authorization of a prescribed process.

7.4   Assurances for senior management

Company directors can now be held personally liable for environmental damage caused by mismanagement. In May 1993, the Environmental Law Foundation, on behalf of Residents Against Incinerator Nuisance (RAIN), successfully approached the London Waste Regulatory Authority to prosecute an incinerator company accused of operating a hospital incinerator in breach of its licence. Not only was the company fined £6,000 and ordered to pay £5,500 in costs, but also the site manager and the company's managing director were given conditional discharges under director's liability for environmental mismanagement.

A significant benefit to directors and managers is the assurance that the environmental aspects of their business are being managed effectively and that no surprises may suddenly emerge.

7.5 Market-place benefits

The Eco-management and audit scheme is a market-based tool; therefore, companies might expect to reap market-place benefits. Banks and insurers are not only increasingly cautious about environmental liabilities but also prefer businesses to be given a seal of approval by a third party organization. As a result, it is anticipated that they will favour sites that can demonstrate their effective management of environmental impacts and effects through registration on the scheme.

Customers may also be encouraged to go to those companies implementing the scheme. The do-it-yourself retailer B&Q is already questioning its suppliers about their environmental performance, as is Boots the chemist, Sainsbury the supermarket chain and the retailer Woolworths. Others will no doubt follow suit. Extensive questions from customers absorb considerable time and effort; the varied nature of the questions themselves often leads to frustration in the respondents. The Eco-management and audit scheme will serve as a clear and credible message to customers that the environmental aspects of the business are managed effectively, reducing the desire of customers to question suppliers.

7.6 Special provision for small and medium-sized enterprises

Efforts have been made within the Regulation to introduce provisions to assist small and medium-sized enterprises' (SMEs) involvement in the Eco-management and audit scheme. Member States may promote company participation of all sizes, but in particular SMEs, by establishing technical assistance which would help these companies meet the scheme's requirements. For example, help in setting up environmental policies, programmes and management systems and preparing environmental statements.

The regulation does not preclude Member States providing financial assistance to companies, although it is unlikely under the present UK government that monies will be forthcoming.

In a recent survey of SMEs implementation of BS 7750, respondents identified the type of support they would like to see introduced to assist environmental management in their companies. Support measures recommended were: government grant assistance for staff and resources to implement environmental management systems, enterprise initiatives, training and awareness seminars and training grants.

The Commission will also look into measures, especially training, structural and technical support, to achieve greater participation of SMEs. No financial assistance measures will be introduced by the Commission.

7.7 Exposing environmental liability

A number of pitfalls may arise from undertaking the Eco-management and audit scheme. Breaches of environmental legislation may be identified during the environmental audit process, which would need to be addressed promptly and prior to registration if the site is to be successful. It is certainty better to be informed about a site's environmental performance rather than learning about it through Greenpeace but once aware of the status quo, management must be fully committed to allocating both human and financial resources to the issues.

During a recession the environment inevitably seems to get pushed down the business agenda; however, once a company has embarked on the Eco-management and audit scheme, a certain quantity of resources will be committed in the medium to long term.

7.8 Controlling environmental information

Several important business implications stem from the environmental statement and the environmental audit report. Clarification is needed on the legal status of the documented information generated by the audit and other processes. At some sites, documented environmental performance information could prove damaging. In the USA, environmental audit reports are routinely protected from discovery using legal privilege, and a lawyer is an important member of the audit team. Nevertheless, fear of damaging reports should not lead a firm to an ostrich-type reaction. What is important, in management terms, is that environmental information is carefully controlled.

CHAPTER 8

CASE STUDIES

8.1 Eco-management and audit scheme applied to local authorities

On an experimental basis, Member States may apply the elements of the Eco-management and audit scheme to local authorities and other public services. In Britain, a trial lasting one year was undertaken to investigate the application of the Eco-management and audit scheme in local government. It was started in March 1992 and funded by the Department of Environment, the Scottish Office and the Local Government Management Board; the study aimed to establish the feasibility and value of adapting the scheme to local government.

Developed under the auspices of the Central and Local Government Environment Forum, the study was essentially concerned with policy impact assessment and management audits rather than the 'state of the environment' audits. The project was divided into two parts and managed by a steering group which included local authority associations, and the Department of the Environment, with project support from CAG consultants.

- Part One: To examine the details of the Regulation and their applicability to local government and the extent of existing environmental management practices in local government.

- Part Two: The development of audit and management procedure guides for local government and their piloting in selected local authorities and specific services.

Professor Janice Morphet, Director of Technical Services at Woking Borough Council, detailed some of the findings of the study at an Environmental Management and Environmental Auditing Research Network (EM&EARN) seminar in March 1993. Over 20 local authorities participated in part one of the study which identified the importance of interpreting the Regulation in a way which was appropriate to the UK public sector. One of the issues that required correct definition and interpretation was the Regulation's focus on sites and how this could be related to the non-site specific functions which local authorities control.

Although local authorities do own sites, most functions are organized along the lines of specific services and departments. Part one of the study concluded that local authorities could be permitted to register individual departments on the scheme but because local authorities also act as a corporate body, it was necessary to gain commitment from the whole corporate body.

To allow for the full application of the scheme across a local authority, the study revealed that it was necessary to be flexible to accommodate the different sizes and procedures which exist in local authorities. To make sure local authorities did implement the scheme over a reasonable time period they would have to prepare assessable plans and targets. If no progress occurred beyond the application of the scheme to a few departments in a local authority, those departments initially registered would be de-registered.

In part two of the study, six Eco-management and audit guides were developed for piloting in seven local authorities over six months. The guides were:

1.   Introduction and Overview.

2.   Corporate Overview and Co-ordination.

3.   Production Effects.

4.   Generic Guide to Services.

5.   Housing Services.

6.   Economic Development Services.

Seven local authorities were selected, a cross-section representing different size, location and experience, and including authorities which had no experience of auditing. The seven pilot local authorities were:

•   Bassetlaw District Council.

•   City of Glasgow District Council.

•   Cleveland County Council.

•   Leeds City Council.

•   London Borough of Hackney.

•   North Wiltshire District Council.

•   Ross and Cromarty District Council.

The aims of part two of the study were to identify:

•   the feasibility and usefulness of the Eco-management and audit scheme modified for local authority use and the usefulness of recommendations in the Guides

- the changes needed in the Regulation and the guides based on the pilot experience

- any structural and/or design modifications to the guides and accompanying worksheets.

Results of pilot

Initial pilot study findings were collated in March 1993 and the key findings were:

- the Eco-management and audit scheme could be incorporated into existing management systems

- the Eco-management and audit scheme provided a useful framework and a means to establish improvement targets

- uncertainties surround the role of the accredited environmental verifier

- the process outlined in the scheme was more important than the statement of participation, consequently participants were unenthusiastic about accreditation

- staff training was essential

- original guides overwhelmed staff

- worksheets were more user-friendly.

As a result of the pilot findings, a modified single guide will be published by HMSO and launched on 14 October, 1993. The guide takes the form of interleaved worksheets with supplementary notes which act as a tool to assist the user implementing the Eco-management and audit scheme. A modified Eco-management and audit scheme adapted to the specific circumstances of local authorities is appended to the guide.

Woking Borough Council profile

Relationship with county: One of 11 Boroughs in Surrey County Council region which will come under review by the Local Government Commission in 1995/6.

Location: Within the metropolitan Green Belt of London to the south-west of London in Surrey.

Attributes: Woking is its main town centre, surrounded by smaller villages. Has a population of 86,000 and is in the London commuter belt.

Employees:	Approximately 600.

Environmental issues:	Increasing traffic volumes especially due to the M25 causing congestion, noise and air pollution; river pollution incidents on the Borough's two major rivers: Bourne and Wey, inherited legacy of contaminated land from disused landfilled sites, important areas of wildlife habitat including Sites of Special Scientific Interest (SSSI).

Local authority issues:	As a large organization consuming large quantities of goods, materials, services and energy it can potentially reduce its environmental impact and create a market for environmentally-friendlier products; as a large employer it has responsibility for establishing a good working environment; it is a representative body for the community and can therefore influence both state and private sectors.

Environmental actions:	The Borough has recognized the growing importance of environmental issues at a local, national and global level and initiated a programme of environmental initiatives which can be likened to the requirements under the Eco-management and audit scheme (Figure 8.1). An Environmental Charter was developed and adopted, at the end of 1990, consisting of six primary statements with supporting initiatives. Environmental values and objectives are being incorporated into the Council's Business Plan.

In November 1990 the Borough commissioned an initial environmental audit from Wardell Armstrong, costing approximately £25,000. Two reports were produced: a State of the Environment Report of the local environment and a Policy Impact Assessment report analysing the environmental impacts of Council policies. Policy recommendations were identified and departmental responsibilities assigned with implementation timetables for action.

A public summary report was produced from the initial environmental audit: *Woking Borough Council Environmental Audit Summary Report* (1991). An interim management review has been undertaken to establish how far policy recommendations are being met. The next full environmental audit will be undertaken in 1994 and a Borough environmental strategy with more specific targets is being developed.

Figure 8.1 – *The Eco-management and audit scheme applied to Woking Borough Council*

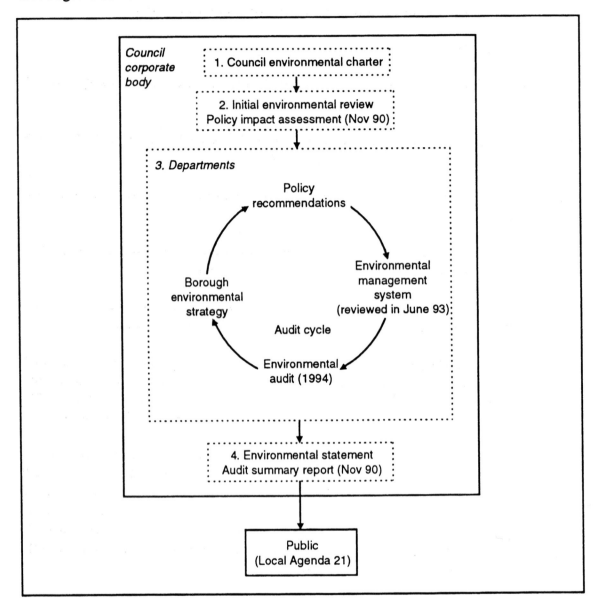

Excerpt from Woking Borough Council's Environmental Charter:

Charter Statements

1. The Borough and Council will maintain, develop and encourage policies which protect and enhance the environment.

2. The Borough and Council will promote recycling of waste materials and the use of recycled or reusable products where economically viable.

3. The Borough and Council will set a good example by pursuing their

own functions in an environmentally responsible manner.

Examples of related initiatives to the above Charter Statements:

Related Initiatives

1a.   An Action Plan based on the aims of the Charter and findings of the Audit.

1b.   Council Committees to review existing policies and develop future ones having regard to the Charter and Audit.

2a.   The Council to respond as far as possible to public demand for recycling facilities.

2b.   The Council to move progressively towards the Government's goal of 50% of recyclable domestic waste being recycled.

3a.   The Borough and Council to have regard to environmental values, as well as value for money, in purchasing goods and services.

3b.   The Council's petrol engine vehicles to run on unleaded petrol as soon as possible, and staff with leased cars will eventually have only cars adapted for unleaded fuel and fitted with catalytic converters. Other organizations in the Borough would be encouraged to follow this line.

Table 8.1 shows examples of Woking Borough Council policy recommendations derived from the initial environmental audit in November 1990. These covered environmental protection, including all media, transport, waste management and recycling, land use planning and leisure, natural environment including SSSIs, energy use and general environmental policies. Policy recommendations not only detail the issues but also assign responsibility and set timetables for action.

Table 8.1 – *Selected summary policy recommendations from Woking Borough initial environmental audit*

Policy recommendations	Responsible department	Current status	Implementation timetable
Noise policy recommendation			
Aim to reduce the levels of noise nuisance experienced by the Borough's residents, where above acceptable levels	Environmental Health Department	24 hour noise nuisance response service in operation. Possibility of proactive monitoring in the future	Ongoing function
Waste management policy recommendations			
Investigate the potential for wheelie bins to increase the amount of domestic refuse collected	Environmental Services	Review and implement once existing waste collecting contract expires in 1996	Review in 1995
Develop and implement a purchasing policy for recycled products	Environmental Services	Purchasing policies have been completed and are being considered for implementation	Mid 1993
Land use, planning and leisure policy recommendations			
Green Belt boundary should be maintained as presently defined and encroachment of development beyond the present urban area should not be permitted	Town Planning	Encroachment of the Green Belt is not permitted	Ongoing function
The Council should consider designating two additional Conservation Areas	Town Planning	Council designated 14 additional Conservation Areas	Implemented
Natural environment policy recommendations			
Identify and formally designate wildlife features of value in the Borough as a wildlife network including wildlife corridors, wildlife links and wildlife action areas	Town Planning	Need for more surveys. Surrey Wildlife Trust are currently surveying a few sites in the Borough	Ongoing function
Develop a programme for the creation of new semi-natural wildlife habitats on urban open space to cover 10% of the area managed by the year end of five years	Leisure Services	Under consideration	Mid 1996

Table 8.1 – continued

Policy recommendations	Responsible department	Current status	Implementation timetable
Energy policy recommendations			
Adopt the Surrey Energy Group Policy Statement	Corporate	Adopted, also Building Services Manager is current Chairman of the Surrey Energy Group	Implemented
Initiate a programme for increasing energy efficiency in Council housing stock	Building Services, Building Control and Housing Section	Implemented	Ongoing function
Water quality policy recommendations			
Where feasible require the permission of separate surface water and foul sewerage drainage systems in the design of new developments	Drainage Section	Implemented. Surface water and foul sewerage are separate in all new developments	Ongoing function
Cease use of Atrazine and Simazine	Corporate	Implemented	Implemented
Transport and vehicle policy recommendations			
All vehicles purchased should specify unleaded petrol engines, fitted with three-way catalytic converters, where available	Finance Office	The majority (95%) of all new leased cars are fitted with a three-way catalytic converter and operate on unleaded petrol	Ongoing function
A phased programme of cycle routes should be implemented over a two year period	Technical Services	Delayed due to financial constraints	1994/5

Woking Borough Council has adopted a proactive strategy towards managing their environmental performance, establishing and implementing elements along the lines of the Eco-management and audit scheme. Undertaking environmental auditing and reporting the findings to the public form a key component of their strategy.

Numerous other local authorities have undertaken some form of environmental audit. The 1992 *Environmental Practice in Local Government* report shows that some 76% of County councils and 33% of London local authorities have undertaken or are undertaking audits to assess environmental issues (more details are shown in Table 8.2). Local authorities, however, have to contend with a number of other pressures which compete for limited human and financial resources. Two significant issues are the current Local Government Commission review of local government and the requirement to introduce compulsory competitive tendering which, according to Professor Janice Morphet, could prove to be environmentally 'blind'.

Table 8.2 – *Environmental auditing activity in Local Government*

Environmental auditing activity	County councils	London boroughs	Metropolitan councils
Completed audit	11 (30%)	3 (9%)	8 (22%)
Audit in progress	17 (46%)	8 (24%)	6 (17%)
Planned audit	5 (14%)	4 (12%)	6 (17%)
No action	4 (11%)	18 (55%)	16 (44%)
Total	**37**	**33**	**36**

Nevertheless, as local authorities prepare their Local Agenda 21 plans as a consequence of the 1992 UNCED conference in Rio de Janeiro, the Eco-management and audit scheme could form an essential and fundamental element in these plans.

8.2 Lessons from the Eco-management and audit scheme pilot study

In April 1992, the Commission initiated a one year pilot study investigating the implementation of the Eco-management and audit scheme in 17 companies across six EC countries. The objectives of the pilot study were:

•   to work through the steps of the Eco-management and audit scheme to assess how it operates in practice

•   to investigate how easy it is for companies to comply with the requirements of the scheme and identify any problems

•   to assess how applicable the general Eco-management and audit scheme framework is to the specific circumstances of different industrial sectors, sizes of companies and different Member States.

Participation in the pilot study was voluntary. No financial assistance was provided by the Commission although PA Consulting Group, a UK-based consulting firm, was retained to provide advice and assistance to the participating companies. Sites were selected for the pilot project that were representative of a variety of industrial sectors covered by the Regulation. They had different approaches to managing their environmental performance and were from different sized companies with single site and multi-site operations.

Industrial activities in the pilot study included:

- Aircraft engine manufacture
- Metal finishing

- Car manufacture
- Non-ferrous metals

- Chemicals
- Paints and resins

- Electricity generation
- Pharmaceuticals manufacture

- Extractive industry
- Plastics

- Leather treatment
- Waste incineration

The 17 sites were all located in the EC. The countries represented in the pilot study were:

- Denmark (one company)
- Italy (four companies)

- France (two companies)
- Ireland (one company)

- Germany (three companies)
- UK (six companies)

On-site activities began in October 1992 with initial workshops between site management and PA Consulting Group personnel to introduce the pilot study. Each site fielded a team of two or three people to spearhead the implementation process. Implementation practice varied from site to site depending on the degree of development of the internal environmental management system. Some sites undertook initial environmental reviews whereas others established environmental auditing programmes, but nearly all attempted to write a site environmental statement.

Results of pilot

Companies reported their experiences with the Eco-management and audit scheme piloting in May 1993. Their observations on the scheme included:

83

- Importance of third party verification and public credibility in the scheme.

- Clarity needed on the environmental review and audit methodology; sector-specific guidelines would be of assistance.

- Uncertainty about the content of the environmental statement.

- Uncertainty about who is the public audience for the site's environmental statement and how widely the statement has to be distributed.

- No guidance on the scale or stringency of environmental objectives and targets and environmental standards that need to be set. Sector-specific guidelines could assist.

- Concern about how continuous environmental improvement will be assessed by accredited environmental verifiers.

- Need for training within companies to meet the scheme's requirements.

- The level of resources that were required to implement the scheme were under-estimated by some companies.

- Concern was expressed about who accredited environmental verifiers might be.

The following company profiles illustrate aspects of the implementation process.

Hydro Aluminium Metals Ltd.

Industrial activity:	Recycling of recoverable aluminium by 24 hour processing of aluminium extrusion, crop-ends, etc. in a gas fired furnace and casting into solid billet which is returned to the supplier as quality raw material for extrusion manufacture. Over 12,000 tonnes of aluminium processed per annum.
Location:	On an industrial estate near the small town of Bedwas in rural South Wales.
Relationship with company:	Wholly owned subsidiary of Norsk Hydro a.s. in Norway.
Employees:	35.

Existing site procedures:	Environmental management is linked to health and safety and is part of Total Quality Management. Certified to BS 5750 in February 1992. Commissioned an energy audit in 1992. Involved in the BS 7750 trial as a member of the Non-ferrous Metals Sector Working Group. Industrial activity is a prescribed process list B under the Environmental Protection Act 1990.
Environmental issues:	Carbon dioxide emissions related to gas fuel, energy usage, particulate and volatile organic compound (VOC) emissions from the furnace stack, solid waste disposal from furnace, cooling water disposal, noise nuisance to local residents.
Business issues:	Raw material supplied and aluminium billet returned to the customer attracts no charge. The cost incurred by the customer is for processing alone. Cost control in processing is therefore particularly important if a competitive edge is to be achieved and this control is closely linked to reducing energy consumption and metal loss in waste material. Effective control of gas consumption per unit of metal output and percentage of metal lost in solid waste are directly related to both cost control and environmental performance improvements.
Environmental actions:	Norsk Hydro a.s. has an overriding Mission Statement and Norsk Hydro (UK) Limited has an overall company environmental policy which is currently being revised at the highest level and will be approved by Egil Myklebust, President of Norsk Hydro a.s.. Norsk Hydro (UK) Ltd. undertook a compliance and health and safety review of all its activities, publishing one of the first independently verified environmental reports in October 1990.

Hydro Aluminium Metals joined the Eco-management and audit pilot study in April 1992, finding the BS 7750 implementation process valuable assistance in achieving the goals of the Regulation. A site-specific programme has been developed and objectives and targets set. Its first environmental statement is being developed from the initial environmental review findings.

Excerpt from Environmental Programme at Hydro Aluminium Metals:

- Comply with environmental legislation and standards.

- Minimize energy inputs.

- Ensure adequate communications with employees, local community and other interested parties.

- Constantly review environmental performance.

- Identify training needs.

- Engender a proactive operating practice towards the environment.

- Comply with codes of practice.

Hydro Aluminium Metals recognized that it was necessary to revisit and revise their environmental programme in the light of their findings during their trials of the Eco-management and audit scheme and BS 7750. For this process the loop diagram in the standard is used.

Yamanouchi Ireland Co. Ltd.

Industrial activity:	Manufacturers of two bulk pharmaceutical compounds.
Location:	A greenfield site in Damastown, North County Dublin, Ireland.
Relationship with company:	Yamanouchi Ireland is a subsidiary of the Japanese company Yamanouchi Pharmaceutical.
Employees:	35.
Existing site procedures:	Established and adopted an environmental policy in 1989. In conjunction with Lloyds Register undertook, in 1990, an environmental audit assessing all procedures with potential impact on the environment. Accredited to ISO 9000 in 1992 and approved by the United States Food and Drug Administration. Member of the Federation of Irish Chemical Industry and is committed to the industry's initiative: Responsible Care. Winner of the Irish Award for Good Environmental Management in 1989 and the EC and United Nations' award in 1990.
Environmental issues:	Biological waste water treatment plant and a liquid quench incinerator, both operated within licenced limits but the goal is to go beyond compliance limits to minimize impact on the environment. Air scrubbing and solvent recovery systems are also in place. Open and clear communication with interested parties including local community, schools and journalists.

Business issues:	Pursuit of environmental standards seen as one element of quality.
Environmental actions:	Undertook to implement in an integrated way both BS 7750 and the Eco-management and audit scheme in parallel. Figure 8.2 shows the outcome of Yamanouchi's comparison of the requirements of the two approaches and acts as their implementation plan. Commenced the EC pilot programme in October 1992 and committed approximately three man days a week to it until the end of the pilot study. Intend to allocate at least the same resources until both initiatives have been successfully implemented. Developed a site environmental profile in three tiers which will be used to formulate a register of significant environmental effects.

- Tier One - Site profile (Figure 8.3)

- Tier Two - Individual sector profiles, e.g. process buildings, maintenance (Figure 8.4)

- Tier Three - Specific equipment profiles

Set up an on-going issues file and are developing Standard Operating Procedures (SOP) identifying that over 100 will need to be produced. Identified and sourced both relevant EC and Irish legislation and compiled into a register with procedures for review and updating. Are developing and updating Yamanouchi's environmental management system establishing essential procedures and selecting elements where activities need to formalized with written procedures, i.e., SOP.

Figure 8.2 – *Yamanouchi Ireland Co. implementation plan*

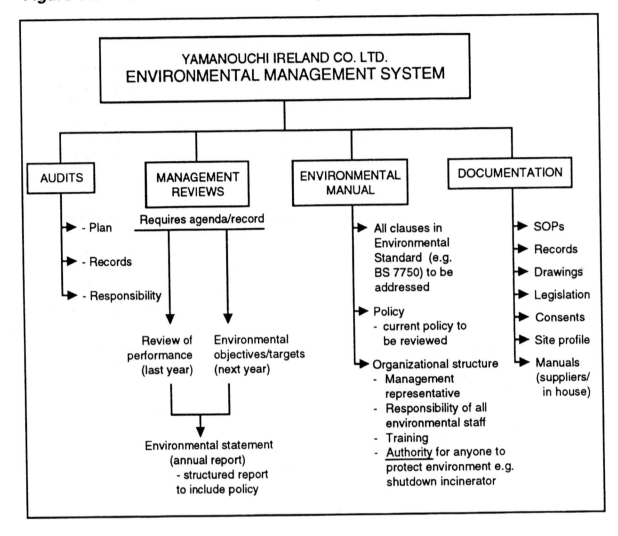

Figure 8.3 – Yamanouchi site environmental profile

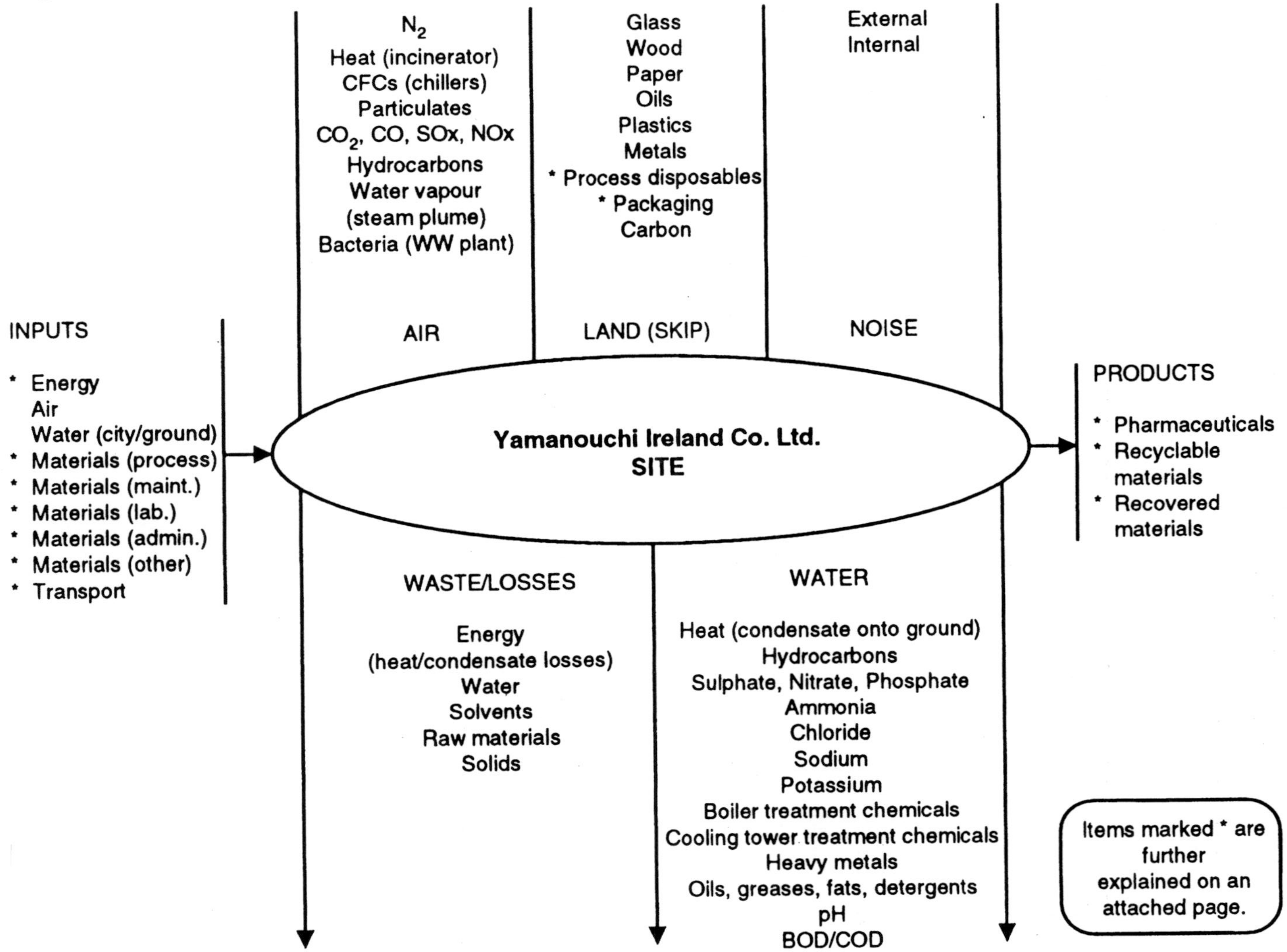

INPUTS

* Energy
  Air
* Water (city/ground)
* Materials (process)
* Materials (maint.)
* Materials (lab.)
* Materials (admin.)
* Materials (other)
* Transport

AIR

N_2
Heat (incinerator)
CFCs (chillers)
Particulates
CO_2, CO, SO_x, NO_x
Hydrocarbons
Water vapour
(steam plume)
Bacteria (WW plant)

LAND (SKIP)

Glass
Wood
Paper
Oils
Plastics
Metals
* Process disposables
* Packaging
  Carbon

NOISE

External
Internal

Yamanouchi Ireland Co. Ltd.
SITE

WASTE/LOSSES

Energy
(heat/condensate losses)
Water
Solvents
Raw materials
Solids

WATER

Heat (condensate onto ground)
Hydrocarbons
Sulphate, Nitrate, Phosphate
Ammonia
Chloride
Sodium
Potassium
Boiler treatment chemicals
Cooling tower treatment chemicals
Heavy metals
Oils, greases, fats, detergents
pH
BOD/COD

PRODUCTS

* Pharmaceuticals
* Recyclable
  materials
* Recovered
  materials

Items marked * are
further
explained on an
attached page.

Figure 8.4 – Yamanouchi process-building profile

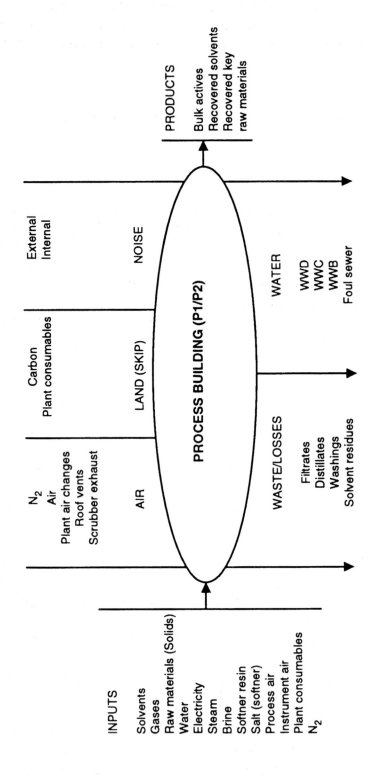

Novotex a.s.

Industrial activity:	Textile firm knitting and manufacturing high-quality cotton garments using combed cotton only. Produces a range of cotton garments called Green Cotton. Close links with companies which perform dyeing and printing functions.
Location:	Western region of Denmark in Ikast.
Relationship with company:	Company operates two closely linked sites.
Employees:	100.
Existing site procedures:	Initially developed its environmental policy in 1986 with its full policy being implemented in 1988. Novotex's policy requires products to be assessed from cradle to grave and places them on an Environmental Value Scale from 0 to 100, with 100 representing the 'totally green product'. Was awarded the Danish Environment Prize for Industry for the development of Green Cotton in 1987. Undertook an initial environmental review in 1992.
Environmental issues:	The textile industry is generally regarded as a heavy polluter and user of water and energy. Energy conservation, waste minimization and emissions to the environment are key issues for the textile industry. Environmental pollution results from using defoliants in machine picked cotton, consequently only 100% hand-picked cotton is used. Cotton production uses many insecticides and herbicides; efforts are being made to use more organically grown cotton with 10% of yarn being organically grown in 1992.
	Dust emissions are reduced by using computerized spinning machines and the use of high quality yarns minimizes waste. Energy conservation features have been incorporated into a new knitting mill. Dyeing, finishing and printing are undertaken by other companies but Novotex works closely with them to reduce their environmental impact. For example, all cooling water is recycled in the dyeing and finishing process and all dyestuff used is 100% water soluble.
Business issues:	Recognition of the fact that it is impossible to manufacture a totally green product but committed to improving existing products and developing new products which minimize environmental impact throughout their life cycles.

Environmental actions: Managing director, Leif Nørgaard, takes responsibility for the company's environmental issues and is extending the company's use of life cycle analysis of its Green Cotton products to establish formal environmental management systems and programmes. Public disclosure of environmental information is an important part of the Novotex approach to producing documents on environmental auditing, life cycle analysis and cleaner production. The latter is produced in conjunction with United Nations Environment Programme's Industry and Environment Cleaner Production Programme.

Leif Nørgaard is a member of The Expert Group for Eco-labelling of Textiles. Novotex was the first company to attempt a life cycle analysis of a cotton T-shirt producing a Green Cotton T-shirt for Earth Day (shown in Table 8.3).

Table 8.3 – *Lifecycle analysis of one Earth Day green cotton T-shirt*

		Rest Grammes	Waste/ losses %	Energy consumption Megajoules	Gas consumption Megajoules
Green Cotton	Process				
Raw Cotton		1000			
	Ginning		64.5 (55 seeds 9.5 losses)	0.8	
Ginned Cotton		353			
	Spinning		24.8	5.16	
Yarn		265			
	Knitting		4	3.67	
Greige Goods		254			
	Dyeing and Finishing		10.6 (5 to edges)	1.76	10.83
Fabrics		227			
	Cutting		14.75	1.16	
T-shirt		192			

Rover Group's Suppliers

Industrial activity: All suppliers to Rover Group. Various industrial activities including upholstery, urethane mouldings, automotive engineering components, coating and resins, aluminium foundry and pressings and assemblies.

Location: Birmingham area.

Relationship with company: Six Rover suppliers were selected to implement BS 7750 and the Eco-management and audit scheme (shown in Table 8.4). The sample companies were varied in size, location and industrial activity and each was given a code name for confidentiality. Two were part of large multi-nationals and two were family companies. The project was managed by a steering group with representative from Rover and Birmingham City Council

Employees: Range from 50 to 600.

Existing site procedures: Rover has a policy of working closely with its suppliers as a way of ensuring quality and making it possible for suppliers to adapt to meet new requirements. Five out of the six companies are registered to BS 5750, the quality systems standard, the sixth is working towards BS 5750.

Environmental issues: Rover's aim was to assist with the improvement of the environmental performance of its suppliers which would contribute to improving the environmental performance of its cars. Birmingham City Council was concerned with helping companies adapt to new market needs and therefore stay in business and maintain employment as well as improving the local authority's local environment.

The pilot study in six companies was to be used to develop good practice guidelines for other suppliers. Specific measures of success were set for the pilot study including identifying how effective both approaches were at improving environmental performance; identifying how complex they were to introduce and showing what were the capital and running costs of implementation.

Business issues: The car industry is experiencing intense competition and is reducing its supplier base. Flexibility and specialisation are key factors and Rover is working closely with its suppliers to ensure quality and meet its market requirements.

Table 8.4 – *Six Rover suppliers participating in the pilot project*

Company	Product category	Employee range	BS 5750 registered
Ash	Pressings and associated assemblies	50 to 100	Yes
Beech	Automotive engineering components	200 to 300	Yes
Birch	Aluminium foundry	500 to 600	Yes
Cedar	Seats and upholstery	200 to 300	No
Pine	Urethane mouldings engineering of plastics	100 to 200	Yes
Poplar	Automotive industrial coatings and resins	300 to 400	Yes

Environmental actions: The project started in Autumn 1991. A main steering group helped company steering groups with the implementation. Initial environmental reviews were conducted by company review teams made up of a company champion, technical and business support from Birmingham City Council, technical support from Rover and students from local technical colleges and universities.

Main findings:

• The requirements of both approaches can be met if resources are made available. Participating companies would have found it very difficult to make progress if support was not available. Pump priming is necessary to help SMEs implement both BS 7750 and the Regulation.

• Interpretation of both BS 7750 and the Eco-management and audit scheme was difficult and SMEs not part of larger multi-national companies found the concepts difficult to understand.

• Concern was expressed about the content of environmental statements; some companies believed the details of the statement could reveal competitive information in a very competitive sector.

Benefits:

• Heightened awareness of environmental issues.

• Improvements in quality of the products.

- Improvements in environmental performance.

- Cost savings ranging from £10,000 to £80,000 mainly from energy cost reduction and to a lesser extent recycling and reductions in waste.

CHAPTER 9

THE FUTURE

9.1 Review of the Eco-management and audit scheme

Not more than five years after the Eco-management and audit scheme enters into force, in July 1998, the Commission is obliged to review the Regulation in the light of experience gained during its operation. The Commission will review the whole Regulation, preamble, articles and annexes and can propose appropriate amendments to the Council of Ministers. Amendments could include the introduction of an Eco-management and audit logo which was in the Commission's original proposal of March 1992 but got lost during political negotiations, and the extension of the scheme to non-industrial sectors which is currently being run on an experimental basis.

9.2 Could a voluntary scheme mutate into a mandatory one?

A considerable amount of anxiety has been expressed by companies that the voluntary nature of the Eco-management and audit scheme is only temporary and that the real intention of the Commission is to establish a mandatory scheme when the Regulation comes up for review in July 1998. The argument runs as follows: if the Commission believes the scheme has had a poor uptake it will argue that it needs to be mandatory to make it effective. Alternatively, if the Commission believes participation in the scheme has been very high it will make the scheme mandatory because there are so few non-participating companies that mandatory status will make little difference to the running of the scheme.

Neither view of the Commission is accurate. The foundation of companies' fear comes from the fact that when the Commission released its consultation document on the scheme, it was to be mandatory (see Section 2.1). The scheme is now a very different animal from when it was first released as a consultation paper in December 1990. Mandatory status was quickly dropped during negotiations with Member States. It will not reappear or be reinstated at the Regulation's review because of one straightforward reason: the Regulation is a market-based instrument designed to harness the power of the market to recognize environmental initiatives undertaken by companies.

For the market to work effectively, transparent credible environmental information is required, thus making it possible to compare and reward companies' environmental performance. Making the Eco-management and audit scheme mandatory goes against the principle of it being a market-based instrument under the EC environmental policy as outlined in its 5th Action Programme on the Environment, *Towards Sustainability*.

9.3 Emerging business issues

Two interlinked strands are propelling businesses to adopt methods to more effectively manage their environmental performance. The steady flow of environmental legislation from both the UK and the EC, coupled with the increasing demand from a variety of sources for corporate disclosure of environmental information, will keep environmental issues on the business agenda.

Ignore these factors at your peril. Companies do get fined for environmental infringements; directors are prosecuted for environmental mismanagement; the public do boycott less environmentally friendly products, especially if targeted by a pressure group; and lenders do refuse loans and insurers do refuse insurance on environmental grounds. A company which responds to these signals and takes action is a proactive company. Such a company will not only avoid prosecutions and bad publicity, but also keep customers and realize business opportunities. Unfortunately, many companies are unaware of their environmental impact and ignorant of the potential penalties.

The Eco-management and audit scheme provides a means for businesses to manage their environmental performance and satisfy the public desire for more environmental information. Ultimately it allows management to be in control.

APPENDIX 1

QUESTIONS AND ANSWERS

The following list of questions has been put to the author by business people during her work on the scheme.

The scheme and registration/de-registration

Q. *When can a company register one of its sites on the Eco-management and audit scheme?*

A. The scheme will be open for company site registration in April 1995.

Q. *When can a company start implementing the elements of the Eco-management and audit scheme?*

A. Now! The final text of the Regulation was adopted on June 29, 1993 and published in the EC's *Official Journal* on July 10, 1993. This report is based on the Regulation and will provide your company with an effective and practical means of understanding the scheme.

Q. *Which companies can apply to the Eco-management and audit scheme?*

A. Any company can apply to the scheme as long as it has overall management control of one or more sites based in the EC and is classified under the industrial activities defined in the Regulation (see Appendix 3).

Q. *Which sites can register on the Eco-management and audit scheme?*

A. Any site can be registered on the scheme as long as it is situated in the EC and conducts industrial activities defined in the Regulation (see Appendix 3).

Q. *Can a site be de-registered from the Eco-management and audit scheme?*

A. Yes, in three ways (see Section 5.3).

Regulation's review: voluntary or mandatory?

Q. *Isn't it a contradiction that the scheme is a Regulation and voluntary?*

A. No, as a Regulation Member States must have the scheme in place for voluntary company participation but once companies join they must follow the Regulation's requirements. A possible analogy: it is voluntary to buy a car but once you own and drive a car you are bound by certain laws such as needing a valid driving licence and road tax.

Q. *Will the Eco-management and audit scheme be reviewed?*

A. Yes, the whole Regulation comes up for review in July 1998 when it would be possible for changes to be introduced.

Q. *Will the EC make the Eco-management and audit scheme mandatory when it comes up for review in 1998?*

A. No, this is against the principle of the scheme as a market-based instrument (see Section 1.3 and 9.2).

Competent body

Q. *Is the competent body required to inspect a site physically when registering on the Eco-management and audit scheme?*

A. No, the competent body is not designed to replace or duplicate existing enforcement bodies such as Her Majesty's Inspectorate of Pollution.

Q. *Can the competent body charge fees?*

A. Yes, it can charge a registration fee.

Q. *Which organisation is likely to be the UK competent body?*

A. The government favours the UK Eco-labelling Board, which is the competent body for the EC Eco-labelling scheme.

BS 7750

Q. *Is BS 7750 compatible with the Eco-management and audit scheme?*

A. Yes, BS 7750 can be used to satisfy the environmental management systems component of the scheme.

Q. *How much more do I have to do after implementing BS 7750?*

A. BS 7750 is an important stepping stone to achieving the Regulation's requirements but you will need to undertake a site specific initial environmental review (not a specification of BS 7750), complete a full environmental audit of performance at the site and produce a site environmental statement.

The Eco-management and audit scheme's elements

Q. *How far does my site have to go to achieve continuous environmental performance improvements?*

A. No specific levels are defined but environmental impacts do not have to be reduced beyond what is achievable by applying BATNEEC.

Q. *How proactive does the environmental audit have to be?*

A. The site's internal environmental audit needs to establish the need for action. It is management who are then responsible for setting environmental objectives aimed at continuous improvement.

Q. *Does my site have to undertake an environmental audit every year?*

A. Top management will set the audit frequency of each site activity which will vary depending on the activity. All activities must be audited within a maximum audit cycle of three years.

Q. *Do I have to employ consultants to do my site's environmental audit?*

A. No, internal environmental audits can be conducted by staff or consultants.

Q. *Is the environmental audit report made available to the public?*

A. No, it's an internal document.

Q. *When is the first environmental statement produced?*

A. After a site has undertaken its initial environmental review and established the site's environmental programme and management system.

Q. *Can I use the statement of participation on products?*

A. No, the Eco-label is for products.

Benefits and costs

Q. *Has my site undertaken any legislative commitments which could help towards getting on the Eco-management and audit scheme?*

A. Companies which have completed applications for authorization of a prescribed process found they had gathered together environmental information and published it, giving them confidence to tackle the public statement part of the scheme.

Q. *Is it going to be very expensive to implement the Eco-management and audit scheme?*

A. There's no doubt that putting the scheme in place will cost. Estimates vary considerably. Companies in the pilot project have identified cost savings but the real benefits from having the scheme should come from the market, e.g. customers, banks and insurers.

Q.   *Is the scheme really only for big companies?*

A.   No, there were just as many small and medium-sized companies in the pilot project of the scheme as large firms.

Q.   *What benefits will be gained from using the scheme beyond the statement of participation?*

A.   As a market-based tool, the market is expected to reward participating firms, for example customers may make selected purchases based on the scheme. Insurers and banks may also be influenced by the scheme. Some companies involved in the pilot project did identify cost savings.

Accredited environmental verifiers

Q.   *Which organisation is going to be responsible for accreditation?*

A.   Currently, this is under discussion but the government favours the National Accreditation Council for Certification Bodies (NACCB).

Q.   *Can accredited environmental verifiers be individuals?*

A.   Yes, with limited accreditation scope, although it is probable that most verifiers will be organizations.

Q.   *If my application to become an accredited environmental verifier is refused can I appeal?*

A.   Appeals procedures are not specifically written into the Regulation but both individuals and organisations must be given the possibility of a hearing before their accreditation is terminated or suspended.

Q.   *Are accredited environmental verifiers also environmental auditors?*

A.   Accredited environmental verifiers could also be environmental auditors, for example, if a consultancy conducted audits but was also accredited as a verifier. However verifiers **do not** undertake the site's internal environmental audit.

Q.   *Can one organization do both my site's environmental audit and its verification?*

A.   No, the accredited environmental verifier must be independent of the site's environmental auditor.

Q.   *Can the accredited environmental verifier set or alter the site's environmental targets or objectives?*

A.   Absolutely not.   The verifiers have no role to determine site environmental objectives but they will look at the procedures for establishing objectives and make sure no significant environmental issue has been omitted.

Q.   *Is there an appeals procedure if I disagree with the accredited environmental verifier view on my site's environmental statement?*

A.   No formal appeals procedure has been written into the Regulation. Member States need to set up their own appeals procedure.

APPENDIX 2

SOURCES OF INFORMATION

A2.1 Further reading

1. The Body Shop International (1993) *The Green Book 2*, The Body Shop International, Watersmead, Littlehampton, UK.

2. Bragg, S., Knapp, P. and McLean, R. (1993) *Improving Environmental Performance: A Guide to a Proven and Effective Approach*, Technical Communications (Publishing) Ltd, Letchworth, UK.

3. British Standards Institution (1992) *Specification for Environmental Management Systems*, BSI, Linford Wood, Milton Keynes, UK.

4. British Standards Institution (1993) *Draft for Public Comment: Draft British Standard Revision of BS 7750: 1992, Specification for Environmental Management Systems (DC 93/400220)*, BSI, Linford Wood, Milton Keynes, UK.

5. Commission of the European Communities (1990) Council Regulation (EEC) No 3037/90 of 9 October 1990 Statistical Classification of Economic Activities NACE Codes Revision 1, *Official Journal* L293, 24.10.90.

6. Commission of the European Communities (1992) Proposal for a Council Regulation (EEC) allowing voluntary participation by companies in the industrial sector in a Community Eco-audit scheme, *Official Journal* C76, Vol. 35, 27.3.92.

7. Commission of the European Communities (1992) *Proposal for a Resolution of the Council of the European Communities on a Community programme of policy and action in relation to the environment and sustainable development*, COM (92) 23, Final Vol. 1, 27.3.92.

8. Commission of the European Communities (1992) *Towards Sustainability. A Community programme of policy and action in relation to the environment and sustainable development*, COM (92) 23, Final Vol. 2, 27.3.92.

9. Commission of the European Communities (1993) Council Regulation (EEC) No 1836/93 of 29 June 1993 allowing voluntary participation by companies in the industrial sector in a Community eco-management and audit scheme, *Official Journal* L168, Vol. 36, 10.7.93.

10. Department of Trade and Industry and Department of the Environment (1993) *Consultation paper on the implementation of the EC Eco-Management and Audit Regulation and accreditation arrangements for certification to BS 7750*, Department of Trade and Industry and Department of the Environment, London, UK.

11. International Chamber of Commerce (1991) *ICC Guide to Effective Environmental Auditing*, ICC Publishing, Paris, France.

12. Local Authority Association and Local Government Management Board 2nd ed (1992) *Environmental Practice in Local Government*, Local Government Management Board, Luton, UK.

13. Woking Borough Council (1991) *Environmental Audit Summary Report*, Woking Borough Council, Woking, UK.

A2.2 Useful contacts

1. Commission of the European Communities
   DGXI Environment, Nuclear Safety and Civil Protection
   Industry and Environment Division (A.2)
   200, rue de la Loi
   1049 Brussels
   Belgium

   Tel: (010 32 2) 299 0451

2. Cameron Clark
   Department of Environment
   Room C11/21
   2 Marsham Street
   London SW1P 3PE

   Tel: 071-276 0595

3. Peter Chandler
   Department of Trade and Industry
   151 Buckingham Palace Road
   London SW1W 9SS

   Tel: 071-215 1022

4. Environmental Help line
   (A Department of Trade and Industry telephone enquiry service detailing environmental pollution issues affecting UK business.)

   Tel: 0800 585 794 (Telephone calls are free), operational until March 1994

5. Sue Element
    Central and Local Government Environment Forum
    Environmental Protection Central Division
    Room A 132
    Romney House
    43 Marsham Street
    London SW1P 3PY

    Tel: 071-276 8752

6. Tony Hams
    Local Government Management Board
    Arndale House
    The Arndale Centre
    Luton
    Bedfordshire LU1 2TS

    Tel: 0582-451166

7. British Standards Institution (BSI)
    2 Park Street
    London W1A 2BS

    Tel: 071-629 9000
    Tel: 0908-226888 (for information on standards)

8. Comité Européen de Normalisation (CEN)
    Rue Brederode 2
    B-1000 Brussels
    Belgium

    Tel: (010 32 2) 519 6819

9. HMSO Publication Centre
    PO Box 276
    London SW8 5DT

    Tel: 071-873 9090 (Telephone orders)

APPENDIX 3

INDUSTRIAL ACTIVITIES COVERED

A3.1 Other industrial activities

Electricity, gas, steam and hot water production
Recycling, treatment, destruction or disposal of solid or liquid waste

A3.2 Statistical classification of economic activities (NACE) codes

The following list of NACE codes shows the Division, e.g. 10 and Group, e.g. 10.1 descriptions of industrial activities. NACE codes are further subdivided into Classes, e.g. 10.10. They are not listed but can be found in Council Regulation No. 3037/90.

Section C Mining and Quarrying

Subsection CA Mining and Quarrying of Energy Producing Materials

10   Mining of Coal and Lignite; Extraction of Peat

      10.1   Mining and agglomeration of hard coal
      10.2   Mining and agglomeration of lignite
      10.3   Extraction and agglomeration of peat

11   Extraction of Crude Petroleum and Natural Gas; Service Activities Incidental to Oil and Gas Extraction Excluding Surveying

      11.1   Extraction of crude petroleum and natural gas
      11.2   Service activities incidental to oil and gas extraction excluding surveying

12   Mining of Uranium and Thorium Ores

      12.0   Mining of uranium and thorium ores

Subsection CB Mining and Quarrying Except Energy-producing Materials

13   Mining of Metal Ores

      13.1   Mining of iron ores
      13.2   Mining of non-ferrous metal ores, except uranium and thorium ores

14 Other Mining and Quarrying

   14.1 Quarrying of stone
   14.2 Quarrying of sand and clay
   14.3 Mining of chemical and fertilizer minerals
   14.4 Production of salt
   14.5 Other mining and quarrying n.e.c.

Section D Manufacturing

Section DA Manufacture of Food Products; Beverages and Tobacco

15 Manufacture of Food Products and Beverages

   15.1 Production, processing and preserving of meat and meat products
   15.2 Processing and preserving of fish and fish products
   15.3 Processing and preserving of fruit and vegetables
   15.4 Manufacture of vegetable and animal oils and fats
   15.5 Manufacture of dairy products
   15.6 Manufacture of grain mill products, starches and starch products
   15.7 Manufacture of prepared animal feeds
   15.8 Manufacture of other feed products
   15.9 Manufacture of beverages

16 Manufacture of Tobacco Products

   16.0 Manufacture of tobacco products

Section DB Manufacture of Textiles and Textile Products

17 Manufacture of Textiles

   17.1 Preparation of spinning of textiles fibres
   17.2 Textile weaving
   17.3 Finishing of textiles
   17.4 Manufacture of made-up textile articles, except apparel
   17.5 Manufacture of other textiles
   17.6 Manufacture of knitted and crocheted fabrics
   17.7 Manufacture of knitted and crocheted articles

18 Manufacture of Wearing Apparel; Dressing and Dyeing of Fur

   18.1 Manufacture of leather clothes
   18.2 Manufacture of other wearing apparel and accessories
   18.3 Dressing and dyeing of fur; manufacture of articles of fur

Subsection DC Manufacture of Leather and Leather Products

19   Tanning and Dressing of Leather; Manufacture of Luggage, Handbags, Saddlery, Harness and Footwear

    19.1   Tanning and dressing of leather
    19.2   Manufacture of luggage, handbags and the like, saddlery and harness
    19.3   Manufacture of footwear

Subsection DD Manufacture of Wood and Wood Products

20   Manufacture of Wood and of Products of Wood and Cork, Except Furniture; Manufacture of Articles of Straw and Plaiting Materials

    20.1   Sawmilling and planing of wood, impregnation of wood
    20.2   Manufacture of veneer sheets; manufacture of plywood, laminboard, particle board, fibre board and other panels and boards
    20.3   Manufacture of builders' carpentry and joinery
    20.4   Manufacture of wooden containers
    20.5   Manufacture of other products of wood, manufacture of articles of cork, straw and plaiting materials

Subsection DE Manufacture of Pulp, Paper and Paper Products; Publishing and Printing

21   Manufacture of Pulp, Paper and Paper Products

    21.1   Manufacture of pulp, paper and paperboard
    21.2   Manufacture of articles of paper and paperboard

22   Publishing, Printing and Reproduction of Recorded Media

    22.1   Publishing
    22.2   Printing and service activities related to printing
    22.3   Reproduction of recorded media

Subsection DF Manufacture of Coke, Refined Petroleum Products and Nuclear Fuel

23   Manufacture of Coke, Refined Petroleum Products and Nuclear Fuel

    23.1   Manufacture of coke oven products
    23.2   Manufacture of refined petroleum products
    23.3   Processing of nuclear fuel

Subsection DG   Manufacture of Chemicals, Chemical Products and Man-made Fibres

24   Manufacture of Chemicals and Chemical Products

   24.1   Manufacture of basic chemicals
   24.2   Manufacture of pesticides and other agro-chemical products
   24.3   Manufacture of paints, varnishes and similar coatings, printing ink and mastics
   24.4   Manufacture of pharmaceuticals, medicinal chemicals and botanical products
   24.5   Manufacture of soap and detergents, cleaning and polishing preparations, perfumes and toilet preparations
   24.6   Manufacture of other chemical products
   24.7   Manufacture of man-made fibres

Subsection DH Manufacture of Rubber and Plastic Products

25   Manufacture of Rubber and Plastic Products

   25.1   Manufacture of rubber products
   25.2   Manufacture of plastic products

Subsection DI   Manufacture of Other Non-metallic Mineral Products

26   Manufacture of Other Non-metallic Mineral Products

   26.1   Manufacture of glass and glass products
   26.2   Manufacture of non-refractory ceramic goods other than for construction purposes; manufacture of refractory ceramic products
   26.3   Manufacture of ceramic tiles and flags
   26.4   Manufacture of bricks, tiles and construction products, in baked clay
   26.5   Manufacture of cement, lime and plaster
   26.6   Manufacture of articles of concrete, cement or plaster
   26.7   Cutting, shaping and finishing of stone
   26.8   Manufacture of other non-metallic mineral products

Subsection DJ Manufacture of Basic Metals and Fabricated Metal Products

27   Manufacture of Basic Metals

   27.1   Manufacture of basic iron and steel and of ferro-alloys (ECSC)
   27.2   Manufacture of tubes
   27.3   Other first processing of iron and steel and production of non-ECSC ferro-alloys

27.4   Manufacture of basic precious and non-ferrous metals
27.5   Casting of metals

28   Manufacture of Fabricated Metal Products, Except Machinery and Equipment

     28.1   Manufacture of structural metal products
     28.2   Manufacture of tanks, reservoirs and containers of metal; manufacture of central heating radiators and boilers
     28.3   Manufacture of steam generators, except central heating hot water boilers
     28.4   Forging, pressing, stamping and roll forming of metal; powder metallurgy
     28.5   Treatment and coating of metals; general mechanical engineering on a fee or contract basis
     28.6   Manufacture of cutlery, tools and general hardware
     28.7   Manufacture of other fabricated metal products

Subsection DK Manufacture of Machinery and Equipment NEC

29   Manufacture of Machinery and Equipment NEC

     29.1   Manufacture of machinery for the production and use of mechanical power, except aircraft, vehicle and cycle engines
     29.2   Manufacture of other general purpose machinery
     29.3   Manufacture of agricultural and forestry machinery
     29.4   Manufacture of machine-tools
     29.5   Manufacture of other special-purpose machinery
     29.6   Manufacture of weapons and ammunition
     29.7   Manufacture of domestic appliances n.e.c.

Subsection DL Manufacture of Electrical and Optical Equipment

30   Manufacture of Office Machinery and Computers

     30.0   Manufacture of office machinery and computers

31   Manufacture of Electrical Machinery and Apparatus NEC

     31.1   Manufacture of electric motors, generators and transformers
     31.2   Manufacture of electricity distribution and control apparatus
     31.3   Manufacture of insulated wire and cable
     31.4   Manufacture of accumulators, primary cells and primary batteries
     31.5   Manufacture of lighting equipment and electric lamps
     31.6   Manufacture of other electrical equipment n.e.c.

32 Manufacture of Radio, Television and Communication Equipment and Apparatus

32.1 Manufacture of electronic valves and tubes and other electronic components
32.2 Manufacture of television and radio transmitters and apparatus for telephony and line telegraphy
32.3 Manufacture of television and radio receivers, sound video recording or reproducing apparatus and associated goods

33 Manufacture of Medical, Precision and Optical Instruments, Watches and Clocks

33.1 Manufacture of medical and surgical equipment and orthopaedic appliances
33.2 Manufacture of instruments and appliances for measuring, checking, testing, navigating and other purposes, except industrial process control equipment
33.3 Manufacture of industrial process control equipment
33.4 Manufacture of optical instruments and photographic equipment
33.5 Manufacture of watches and clocks

Subsection DM   Manufacture of Transport Equipment

34 Manufacture of Motor Vehicles, Trailers and Semi-trailers

34.1 Manufacture of motor vehicles
34.2 Manufacture of bodies (coachwork) for motor vehicles; manufacture of trailers and semi-trailers
34.3 Manufacture of parts and accessories for motor vehicles and their engines

35 Manufacture of Other Transport Equipment

35.1 Building and repairing of ships and boats
35.2 Manufacture of railway and tramway locomotives and rolling stock
35.3 Manufacture of aircraft and spacecraft
35.4 Manufacture of motorcycles and bicycles
35.5 Manufacture of other transport equipment n.e.c.

Subsection DN   Manufacturing NEC

36 Manufacturing of Furniture; Manufacturing NEC

36.1 Manufacture of furniture

36.2   Manufacture of jewellery and related articles
36.3   Manufacture of musical instruments
36.4   Manufacture of sports goods
36.5   Manufacture of games and toys
36.6   Other manufacturing n.e.c.

37   Recycling

37.1   Recycling of metal waste and scrap
37.2   Recycling of non-metal waste and scrap

APPENDIX 4

LIST OF ABBREVIATIONS

AEC	Association of Environmental Consultants
BATNEEC	Best Available Techniques Not Entailing Excessive Cost
BSI	British Standards Institution
CBI	Confederation of British Industry
CEN	Comité Européen de Normalisation
EARA	Environmental Auditors Registration Association
EC	European Community
ECOSOC	Economic and Social Committee
EOTC	European Organization for Testing and Certification
ESRC	Economic and Social Research Council
EFTA	European Free Trade Association
EM&EARN	Environmental Management and Environmental Auditing Research Network
FMEA	Failure Mode and Effect Analysis
HMIP	Her Majesty's Inspection of Pollution
HMSO	Her Majesty's Stationary Office
ICC	International Chamber of Commerce
IPC	Integrated Pollution Control
ISO	International Standards Organization
ISRS	International Safety Rating System
LIFE	Community Financial Instrument for the Environment
MEP	Member of the European Parliament
NACCB	National Accreditation Council for Certification Bodies
NACE	Nomenclature générale des activitiés économiques dans les Communa Européenes
NRA	National Rivers Authority
RAIN	Residents Against Incinerator Nuisance
SAGE	Strategic Advisory Group on the Environment
SME	Small and Medium-sized Enterprise
SOP	Standard Operating Procedures
SSSI	Site of Special Scientific Interest
VOC	Volatile Organic Compound